Stinging Fly Patrons

Many thanks to: Mark Armstrong, Maria Behan, Niamh Black, John Boyne, Celine Broughal, Trish Byrne, Bruce Carolan, Edmond Condon, Evelyn Conlon, Sean Curran, Edel Fairclough, Michael J. Farrell, Ciara Ferguson, Kathy Gilfillan, Michael Gillen, Brendan Hackett, James Hanley, Christine Dwyer Hickey, Dennis Houlihan, Peggy Hughes, Nuala Jackson, Jerry Kelleher, Conor Kennedy, Gráinne Killeen, Joe Lawlor, Irene Rose Ledger, Wendy Lynch, Róisín McDermott, Petra McDonough, Lynn Mc Grane, Finbar McLoughlin, Maggie McLoughlin, Ama, Grace & Fraoch MacSweeney, Mary MacSweeney, Paddy & Moira MacSweeney, Anil Malhotra, Dáirine Ní Mheadhra, Lucy Perrem, Maria Pierce, Peter J. Pitkin, Fiona Ruff, Alf Scott, Ann Seery, Eileen Sheridan, Alfie & Savannah Stephenson, Mike Timms, Colleen Toomey, Olive Towey, Simon Trewin, Ruth Webster, Gráinne Wilson, The Irish Centre for Poetry Studies at Mater Dei Institute, Lilliput Press, Munster Literature Centre, New Binary Press, Poetry Ireland and Tramp Press.

We'd also like to thank those individuals who have expressed the preference to remain anonymous.

By making an annual contribution of 75 euro, patrons provide us with vital support and encouragement.

Become a patron online at
www.stingingfly.org
or send a cheque or postal order to:
The Stinging Fly, PO Box 6016, Dublin 1.

New Writers, New Writing

The Stinging Fly

issue **31** | Summer 2015
volume **two** | €8.00 / £7.00

LONDON ISSUE

POEMS (CONTINUED)

COVER ART

Oisin Byrne

Michelangelo (2004)
Mixed media on board, 100 x 100 cm.

COVER DESIGN

Fergal Condon

Submissions are currently being sought for a special themed issue in February 2016: 'In the Wake of the Rising', which will be guest edited by Sean O'Reilly. The submission deadline is Friday, August 14ᵗʰ 2015—see the submission guidelines on our website: stingingfly.org

'… God has specially appointed me to this city, so as though it were a large thoroughbred horse which because of its great size is inclined to be lazy and needs the stimulation of some stinging fly…'
—Plato, *The Last Days of Socrates*

Next Issue Due: October 2015

The Stinging Fly
new writers, new writing

Editors
Declan Meade &
Thomas Morris

Publisher
Declan Meade

Design & Layout
Fergal Condon

Editorial Assistant
Fiona Boyd

Poetry Editor
Eabhan Ní Shúileabháin

Eagarthóir filíochta Gaeilge
Aifric MacAodha

Contributing Editors
Emily Firetog, Dave Lordan & Sean O'Reilly

© Copyright remains with authors and artists, 2015

Printed by Naas Printing Ltd, County Kildare

ISBN 978-1-906539-49-8 ISSN 1393-5690

Published three times a year (February, June and October).

The Stinging Fly gratefully acknowledges the support of The Arts Council /
An Chomhairle Ealaíon and Dublin City Council

PO Box 6016, Dublin 1
stingingfly@gmail.com

Keep in touch: sign up to our e-mail newsletter, become a fan on Facebook, or follow
us on Twitter for regular updates about all publications, events and activities.

www.stingingfly.org | www.facebook.com/StingingFly | @stingingfly

Editorial

Following on from our New York issue in 2011, it was, quite rightly, only a matter of time before we switched our attention to London. We put out a call for submissions last October, inviting writers to send us their poems and stories about the city. We also set about asking others to recount their experiences of visiting the city or living there.

London, now more than ever, is right next door. We can get there from Dublin—right into the heart of it—in the same time and often for less money than it takes to get to Cork, Galway or Belfast. My own parents, whose lives are rooted in County Louth, have spent more time in London on family visits this past twenty years than they've spent in any city here at home. And London's over here too, of course, looming ever larger in our shopping centres and on our TV screens.

For all this new closeness and accessibility, many of the pieces we've gathered together in the issue bear testimony to the fact that the relationship that Irish people in London have with the city remains a complex and complicated one. Yes, it offers inspiration and fresh opportunities and new freedoms, but often there is the persistent sense of not being on familiar ground—belonging neither here nor there anymore.

My own experience of London is limited. I went over in the summer after I'd done my Leaving Certificate to stay with my aunt and her family in Bethnal Green and I ended up working for a few weeks as a chambermaid in a hotel near Euston Station. (There might be a story there somewhere but it's buried deep.) More recent trips have centred around siblings and friends and occasional bits of business. I'm all the more grateful, therefore, to Catherine Dunne, whose book *An Unconsidered People* provides such rich insight into the lives of the generation of people who left Ireland during the nineteen-fifties and made London their home. Catherine also introduced me to Charlotte Curran—from the organisation Irish in Britain—who was extremely generous in offering ideas and making further connections.

From reading Catherine's book and talking to Charlotte and to others, I know there is a whole other issue that might be done about the Irish in London. In the meantime, I hope you'll enjoy this one—our biggest yet!

—Declan Meade, June 2015

RE:*fresh* | 'Autumn Journal' by Louis MacNeice
Harry Clifton

The great poems of London, strangely enough, are not written by Londoners. With the exception of William Blake, the rest, from Shakespeare through to Samuel Johnson, William Wordsworth to T.S. Eliot, came in from their various provinces, be they Stratford, Lichfield, the Lake Country or New England— to make names and futures, to be corrupted and to grow up. Johnson's 'London' with its muggers in dark alleys, Wordsworth's young man in 'The Prelude' spellbound by the living freak-show of the city, and the puritan Eliot alchemising fascination and disgust in 'The Waste Land':

> Mr. Eugenides, the Smyrna merchant
> Unshaven, with a pocket full of currants
> C.i.f London: documents at sight,
> Asked me in demotic French
> To luncheon at the Cannon Street Hotel
> Followed by a weekend at the Metropole.

Centuries of disillusioned innocence repeat themselves, one way or another, in these great poems. Until lately, for generations of Irish people, London was where lost virginities, physical, spiritual or political, came to terms with themselves, so it is no surprise that Ireland is the province colonising the capital in Louis MacNeice's 'Autumn Journal' of 1938, the latest so far of the great London meditations. Not, it has to be said, the Ireland of the underdog or economic migrant, but of the intellectual in voluntary exile—a Classics don, a divorcee, a left-leaning secular liberal at the end of youth, at the end of the 1930s, the western world and the private self both with their backs to the wall, in this case the wall of a flat on Primrose Hill overlooking London, as Munich and Hitler fill the newsstands, the park is cleared for anti-aircraft emplacements, and Europe teeters on the edge of war.

> Hitler yells on the wireless,
> The night is damp and still,

And I hear dull blows on wood outside my window:
They are cutting down the trees on Primrose Hill.

If there is a single question dominating the 24 sections of 'Autumn Journal' it is 'How did I, how did the world, arrive at this point?' Section by section, the self-interrogations address themselves to the poet's Irish background, to his love-life, his studies in Greek and Latin, and his immersion, like so many thirties poets, in the Spanish Civil War. Though nothing is forced in this journal of a London autumn, all the above themes, once introduced, are re-stated, as in a symphony, before winter comes and the certainty of war. An earlier poem 'Valediction' had already said goodbye to the closed, childish society of Ireland, but imminent tragedy in Europe strips any residual sentiment from the backward glance.

There is no immunity in this island either;
A cart that is drawn by someone else's horse
And carrying goods to someone else's market.
The bombs in the turnip sack, the sniper from the roof,
Griffith, Connolly, Collins, where have they brought us?
Ourselves alone! Let the round tower stand aloof
In a world of bursting mortar!

The argument against isolationism extends past the Irish Free State to its Nobel laureate Yeats and his pre-modern poetics. 'I would have a poet able-bodied,' writes MacNeice in *Modern Poetry*, 'fond of talking, a reader of the newspapers, capable of pity and laughter, informed in economics, appreciative of women, involved in personal relationships, susceptible to physical impressions.' And he adds, in his prospectus to 'Autumn Journal': 'The writing is direct. Anyone could understand it.' Compare all that with the classical detachment, the impersonality of Yeats's own treatment of western collapse in his poem 'The Gyres':

Irrational streams of blood are staining earth;
Empedocles has thrown all things about;
Hector is dead and there's a light in Troy;
We that look on but laugh in tragic joy.

Not that the Classics do not play a major part in MacNeice's own background and formation, and in the very fabric of 'Autumn Journal'; he had, after all just moved from Birmingham to London University as a lecturer in that subject. But as touchstones of reality, let alone balance, they have a hard time justifying themselves in the age of Gog and Magog, Hitler and Stalin.

> And how one can imagine oneself among them
> I do not know;
> It was all so unimaginably different
> And all so long ago.

Neither Ireland nor Greece, country or culture, have much for the lonely individual to fall back upon, in his hour of need. And the modern ideals, embodied in calls to arms with the International Brigade, in the struggle for republican Spain against Franco, are a bog of compromise where the liberal conscience finds no footing either.

> We have come to a place in space where shortly
> All of us may be forced to camp in time:
> The slender searchlights climb,
> Our sins will find us out, even our sins of omission.

What survives is less a philosophy than a vision of life as a dance of brilliant particulars on a background of failed ideas. Its most famous embodiment ('the drunkenness of things being various') is in his poem of the early thirties 'Snow', but it is everywhere in 'Autumn Journal', where the life of the senses— the smell of bread on Charlotte Street, the clinging foam in a beer-glass, the rose geranium soap in the steaming bath, the bark of a sea-lion in Regent's Park zoo—is marshalled, unconsciously, against the large generalities that have everyone marching in lockstep to disaster.

> Open the world wide, open the senses,
> Let the soul stretch its blind enormous arms,
> There is vision in the fingers only needing waking
> Ready for light's alarms.

'The man who is tired of London,' as Samuel Johnson wrote, 'is tired of life.' Mac Neice, oddly enough, is never less tired of London or life than in the sections of 'Autumn Journal' celebrating an unnamed woman (the painter Nancy Coldstream) with whom his relationship falls apart in the months of its composition. Not since Coleridge's 'Dejection Ode' has a poet so closely analysed the collapse of feeling into its absence; and yet gratitude, not just for what has passed between them, but for the city itself, is the dominant note.

> Who has left a scent on my life and left my walls
> Dancing over and over with her shadow,
> Whose hair is twined in all my waterfalls
> And all of London littered with remembered kisses.

The hardboiled veteran of emotional wars ('When we are out of love, how were we ever in it?') is forever contending with an open-hearted melancholic, never more so than in the section on a Christmas visit to Paris. That city, of course, is the capital of worldly cynicism, as Spain equals political conflict and Ireland an innocence that never grows beyond itself to the wider fate. All these places or states of mind are, however, contained in London itself—the site of final disillusionment, private or public, to be lived through for something new to resume.

By December, as his biographer Jon Stallworthy tells us, much of 'Autumn Journal' had been written, and by early the following February the typescript was with his publisher T.S. Eliot. In the meantime, the equivocatings of 1938 had given way to the grim certainties of 1939. Politically, war was now inevitable; and privately, love was a thing of the past.

> The lady is gone who stood in the way so long,
> The hypnosis is over and no-one
> Calls encore to the song.

At this point, the whole poem shifts away from retrospection and self-examination. The ground has been cleared, the battle about to begin for the fate of mankind. Contemplation, now, gives way to action. The master-image, in the great final section, is of millions sleeping, as in Shakespeare's *Henry V*, on the eve of something decisive.

> To-night we sleep
> On the banks of Rubicon the die is cast;
> There will be time to audit
> The accounts later, there will be sunlight later
> And the equation will come out at last.

It is eighty years, or nearly, since the first publication of 'Autumn Journal'. Did the equation come out at last? Or is something infinitely less liberal and optimistic slouching towards Bethlehem to be born? The war, like the one before it, solved nothing, and subsequent conflicts—the ones on our screens— leave us in the same uneasy peace as 1938, while staking out our greeds and paranoias in farther corners of the earth. Nobody new, in all these years, shows signs of coming through from the provinces with another London meditation. And that, perhaps, is because the one we have in 'Autumn Journal' is more than adequate, living as we do on the edge of a rational catastrophe, armed with the Saturday morning liberal optimism MacNeice unmasked, in himself and others, for its hollowness, while still loving the London it and he belonged to. Irish or not, our backs are still to the wall of that Primrose Hill flat, in that faraway autumn.

MacNeice's London

Hexagonal tables, soundproofed in green baize,
Littered with microphones,
Ashtrays, teacups… Your element, MacNeice,
A glasswalled studio, to be alone in
With a million listeners, there beneath Portland Place

And calling all nations. Go home from your work
And listen in to the voices
Swarming inside you. Try them out on the dark,
On paper, on the walls of your flat
In Primrose Hill, on this girlfriend or that

Who shares your bed and leaves you your bachelorhood
Old as Samuel Johnson's
Wedded to London. Mother went mad
In the Old Sod, and the Celtic Twilight
Sank in the Western Approaches. Regression and flight

Were always old hat. There is only the view from the
    window,
Regent's Park and Marylebone
Leafless on a winter Sunday, with nothing to do,
Only yourself to look into,
Apperceptive, stoical and true,

A string of average days
That come to nothing. See them laddering past
Like London Underground, crammed with speechless faces,
Brief, platonic. What better place
Than London, to mirror the lonely self-regard

Of a stateless person? Lay your cards
On the green baize table, it is deep underground,
A bunker of civilised sound,
A BBC studio… Thirty years dead
I see your ghost, as the Blitz carooms overhead,

Dissolve like a smoke-ring, meditative,
Classic, outside time and space,
Alone with itself, in the presence of the nations,
Well-bred, dry, the voice
Of London, speaking of lost illusions.

Harry Clifton

Pádraic Ó Conaire: Finding sanctuary in exile

Pádraigín Riggs

Patrick Conroy was born in Galway city in 1882, where his father, Thomas, had a public house. His parents both belonged to the upwardly mobile Catholic class who prospered in business, in the professions and in the Church, following the Repeal of the Penal Laws. However, financial difficulties—due, apparently to Thomas's drinking—meant that the family had to move house four times in six years and in 1888, when Patrick was six years old, his father departed for America, abandoning his family. Patrick's mother, Kate, assumed control of the business but, six years later, she died suddenly and Patrick and his two younger brothers were sent to live with their paternal grandparents in Rosmuck, in the Connemara Gaeltacht. When their grandmother died, two years later, he and one of his brothers were sent to live with their maternal aunt in Miltown Malbay, County Clare. A year later, he was uprooted once again, this time to Rockwell College, County Tipperary, where he was enrolled in the seminary. Within a year, the seminary closed and he moved to Blackrock College, in Dublin, which was also run by the Holy Ghost order. His classmates in Blackrock included the young Eamonn De Valera and the future Cardinal Dalton. Patrick Conroy left Blackrock without having completed his final examinations and commenced work as a boy-copyist in the Board of Education at Whitehall, London, in January 1900. He was a month short of being nineteen years old.

While Irish was not his first language, he had a good knowledge of Irish growing up. English was the language of his domestic environment, despite the fact that his father was from Rosmuck. English was associated with status and progress and was the language spoken in the family home in Galway and also in Rosmuck—the Conroys of Rosmuck were very prosperous merchants, trading on boats throughout the Connemara Gaeltacht. However, the young Patrick was exposed to Irish during these years; Irish was spoken in the family public house in Galway where many of the customers came from Connemara, and he and his brothers were looked after by young women from the West who spoke Irish. In Rosmuck, Irish was the language of the community outside of the home and some Irish was also spoken in the part of County Clare where he lived with his aunt. It was hardly surprising that his best grades in the Intermediate Certificate (Junior and Middle), were in Irish (or 'Celtic', as it was called then).

The Gaelic League had been founded in Ireland in 1893 and three years later, a branch was established in London. When the young civil servant, P.J. Conroy, was enrolled as a member in December 1900 he became Pádraic Ó Conaire and from that time until his return to Ireland in 1915, the Gaelic League played a central role in his life. Through his association with the organisation in London he got to know Irish emigrants from all social classes: native speakers of Irish, scholars of the language and those who had joined the League in order to learn Irish. He soon became active in its various sub-committees, participated in its cultural activities, performing in—and even writing—short plays. As well as being a useful language-teaching tool, drama provided an opportunity for meeting people and feeling part of a cultural community. Ó Conaire also gave lectures on various topics and began teaching at the Irish classes throughout London. He became a committed activist on behalf of the language and very soon acquired a reputation as an accomplished speaker of Irish, an inspiring teacher and, above all, a successful writer. The domestic instability that he experienced when growing up in Ireland seems to have set a permanent pattern; he moved house frequently—for example, between 1905 and 1911 his four children were born and the address on each child's birth certificate is different. It is significant that the only permanent address he himself had during the time he lived in London was that of the Gaelic League—as if that was his real home.

In the Irish-speaking milieu that was the London Gaelic League, Ó Conaire enjoyed friendship, encouragement and respect. By 1902 he had mastered the Berlitz system of language teaching which the London Gaelic League was promoting in its classes and by 1905 he was instructing the other teachers in the system. By this time he was also teaching Irish under the auspices of the London County Council. In 1904, he was teaching Irish every evening of the week—as well as working in the civil service (where his post was not overly demanding or stimulating—or well-remunerated). His fee from the LCC amounted to almost half the salary he was earning in the civil service.

Ó Conaire's colleagues and friends in the London Gaelic League were readers and the milieu to which he now belonged was one where contemporary literature was discussed. While it is not possible to say what he read, he refers, in his 1908 prize-winning essay 'Sean-litríocht na nGael agus nua-litríocht na hEorpa', to Gogol, Turgenev, Andreyev, Gorky, Tolstoy, Ibsen, Bjornsen and Knut Hamsun. He also mentions Hardy, Meredith, Maupassant and Balzac. He published his first short story in *An Claidheamh Soluis* in 1901 and by the following year had written a short play. He claims that it was the Tipperary-born journalist and prominent Gaelic Leaguer, William P. Ryan, who encouraged him to write in Irish rather than in English. It is not possible to say whether or not he had already started writing in English but from the time he published his first story in 1901 he wrote exclusively in Irish. Between 1904 and 1913 he won prizes in the Oireachtas Literary Competition for short stories, for one-act plays, for essays on literary topics and for his only novel, *Deoraíocht* (published in 1910). The Oireachtas competitions and the various Gaelic League periodicals, both in London and in Dublin, provided him with an outlet for his work and also augmented his modest income. Pádraic Pearse, who was secretary of the League's publication committee from 1899 and editor of *An Claidheamh Soluis* from 1903 was a very important mentor and source of encouragement for the young writer.

By 1913, politics were beginning to have an effect on the cultural and literary activities of the Gaelic League both in Ireland and in London. *An tÉireannach*, the monthly paper of the London branch, had ceased to exist for financial reasons in the previous October, which meant that for the first time since the establishment of *Inis Fáil*, in 1904, the London League was without a regular publication. By 1915, the Irish London's attention turned to Dublin. As Art Ó Briain wrote (1944, *Capuchin Annual*): 'From the outbreak of the war in 1914, all activities of the London League were on the wane, and in 1917, when so many of the "Wild Geese" had flown back to Ireland, the number of schools had declined to four. Even these only maintained a, more or less, symbolic existence, with perhaps only one class and a few pupils.'

Ó Conaire was dismissed from his post in the civil service in October 1915— apparently because he returned late from Ireland where he was attending the Gaelic League Ard-Fheis. However, he had been contemplating leaving London for some time before that. His friends and associates were gradually returning to Ireland from as early as 1912, and the community that had sustained him in London was disintegrating. He now believed passionately in the idea of an Irish-speaking Ireland and was convinced that he could realise his dream if he returned. He wrote in the magazine *Samhain*, in November 1915:

> The Irish language movement will not thrive until every English speaker, whether he be sympathetic or otherwise, realises that he is a foreigner in his own country if he speaks English. And I believe that the movement

will make no progress until some small group undertakes to speak Irish exclusively and on every possible occasion.

Ó Conaire departed for Dublin in December 1915, one month before his Gaelic-League friend Michael Collins (with whom he joined the Irish Volunteers in 1913) did the same. He wrote later of the conversation that ensued when the pair met again in January 1916. It was clear that both men were thinking of a revolution, but for Ó Conaire it would be a language revolution.

Pádraic had hoped to live as a full-time writer when he returned to Ireland, with the support of the Gaelic League but, as we've seen, that organisation had taken a new direction by 1915 and providing maintenance for a writer was low on its list of priorities. He received a small allowance from the Executive Council for about fifteen months, in return for short articles he wrote for *An Claidheamh Soluis* but these articles appear to have ceased from March 1917. By now he was no longer in receipt of a regular income—however meagre— from the civil service. His drinking had become problematic at this time also. He found himself reduced to writing harmless material for school textbooks for a while, in order to eke out a living, and for the last three years of his life his publications consisted exclusively of short weekly articles for *The Connacht Sentinel*. Prophetically, like so many of the characters in his stories who returned from exile, the life to which he returned proved to be a bitter disappointment.

Between 1901 and 1927, he published some 400 short stories, 200 short journalistic articles, six one-act plays and one novel. A total of twenty collections of his short fiction and essays were published. Of these works, three collections of short stories have been translated and published in English: *The Land of Wonders* (1919), *The Woman at the Window* (1921) and *Field and Fair* (1929). A further collection, *The Finest Stories of Pádraic Ó Conaire*, aimed at Leaving Cert students who were studying *Scothscéalta*, was published in 1982. The novel *Deoraíocht* was published in English as *Exile* (1994) and in Czech as *Vyhnanstvi* (2004). Although this oeuvre seems substantial, the actual amount of material that comprises his literary output is relatively small: many works appeared in more than one collection and some reappeared a number of times in different papers. Apart from one collection of seven stories which had the 1916 Rising as a unifying theme, and which was published in 1918, Ó Conaire's best work was all written while he lived in London.

There are different perceptions of Pádraic Ó Conaire. For many Irish people, he is the author of the story 'M'asal Beag Dubh'—a fondly remembered school text. For others, he is the larger than life character who was familiar on the roads of Ireland between 1915 and 1928, when he was struggling to earn a meagre existence from his journalism or from some short irregular teaching posts, drinking heavily and becoming increasingly dependent on the charitable assistance of his friends. Few think of Ó Conaire as a writer of sophisticated modern psychological fiction.

Exile is a recurring theme in his work and this theme has tended to be read as autobiography. In fact, although he produced this work while he was living in London, London—as a geographical location—has no place in his stories. He writes about a condition of internal exile where London is merely a metaphor. Invariably, it is the characters who return home that prove to be the real exiles. The psychological condition that William James described as 'The Divided Self' is the theme of stories such as 'Páidín Mháire' in which a simple fisherman has to exchange the freedom of his life by the sea for the prison that is the Workhouse, or 'Nóra Mharcais Bhig', in which a young pregnant girl has to exchange her life in a village in Connemara for the life of a prostitute in London, or in the stories of *An Chéad Chloch*, that are purportedly set in an oriental country or in the land of the Bible. The novel, *Deoraíocht*, which could be translated as 'exile' (or 'alienation') is set in London and Galway but this 'London' is merely an internal state; London is never described and no recognisable landmarks or streets are named. It is a place that is not Galway, just as 'Galway' is a place that is not London. That is, each place is defined as the obverse of the other: London is the present, a place associated with loss and damage while Galway is the past—a state of innocence and hope, a Paradise Lost to which there is no happy return. Like many emigrants, Ó Conaire returned to an Ireland that was changing radically and the vision of home that he had conceived while he was in London never materialised.

Pádraic Ó Conaire, the writer, would have benefitted from the sustained support of an editor such as Pádraic Pearse, and from an informed, critical readership. Unfortunately, he was denied both. Nevertheless, his best work merits inclusion in any anthology of Irish short fiction from the beginning of the last century, in either language. And, in the past nine years, three collections of Ó Conaire's best work have been reprinted, with a short introduction in each case: *An Chéad Chloch*, published by Mercier (2006), and *Scothscéalta* (2009) and *Rogha Scéalta* (2008), both published by Cló Iar-Chonnacht. As the first writer in the Irish language to produce modern short fiction which endures one hundred years later, his legacy is significant.

From the Heroic to the Elegiac:
Portrayals of the Post-War Irish Navvy in London
Tony Murray

O, Camden Town; O, Camden Town, you stole my youth away
For I was young and innocent, and you were old and grey
>   from *Hut 42* by John B. Keane

Shortly before Christmas 2003, at the peak of the economic boom in Ireland, something nudged at the conscience of a newly prosperous nation. A documentary was screened on primetime Irish television about the onerous plight of elderly Irish men in Britain. Their impoverishment was a salutary reminder of the potential consequences of something that appeared to no longer be a feature of Irish society, namely, emigration. Some of the men interviewed had spent the majority of their working lives on the building sites of London. But due to increased mechanisation in the construction industry over the previous two decades and the insecure terms of their employment, these former navvies were now living out their final days in destitution in the very neighbourhoods they helped rebuild after the Second World War.

They were the generation who in the middle decades of the twentieth century had to leave Ireland because it had failed on the social and economic promises of independence. The sense of nationhood envisaged by de Valera as 'joyous with the sounds of industry', rather than being realised in the fields and 'cosy homesteads' of Ireland had to be reimagined on the building sites and hospital wards of Britain. But whilst a ubiquitous presence on the streets of London for many decades after the Second World War, the Irish navvy, paradoxically left a somewhat anonymous and enigmatic legacy in the social history of his adopted city. As one of the characters in John B. Keane's novel, *The Contractors*, declares: 'We dig the tunnels, lay the rails and build the roads and buildings. But we leave no other sign behind us. We are unknown and unrecorded.'

As such men are displaced by their latter-day equivalents from Latvia and Bulgaria, we are witnessing the denouement to a particularly resonant chapter in the history of Irish migration. The poignancy of this moment has been captured well in stage-plays like Jimmy Murphy's *Kings of the Kilburn High Road* and Owen McCafferty's *The Absence of Women*. Fictional accounts about Irish navvies in London have generally, however, had less impact. Novels such as J.M. O'Neill's *Open Cut*, Philip Casey's *The Water Star* and Peter Woods's *Hard Shoulder* explore important dimensions of this experience, but they are not widely known. Perhaps the most familiar example of the genre is indeed *The Contractors* which reached the bestseller lists on both sides of the Irish Sea in 1994. Like popular ballads such as 'McAlpine's Fusiliers', it is a rousing and entertaining story which suggests that, during the nineteen-fifties and sixties at least, the lot of the London Irish navvy was a buoyant and optimistic one. What made the TV images screened forty years later so shocking, perhaps, was the fact that the Irish navvy had been regularly presented in this way in popular culture.

Most of the action of *The Contractors* takes place in the typical surroundings of the building site, dancehall or 'digs'. Here, within a migrant netherworld of subbies, gangers and 'the lump', unspoken rural codes and practices of masculinity are refigured in an urban ethnic context. In a thinly disguised reference to Murphy and McNicholas, the novel's central plotline is the enmity between two construction firms, one from Kerry and one from Mayo. As the story develops, personal as well as collective rivalries are played out in an impending atmosphere of verbal and physical violence. When a major fight takes place on St Patrick's Night between the two gangs of navvies, the car park of an Irish dancehall becomes the arena for fiercely held county allegiances. Indeed, it acquires the mythical significance of an ancient battleground as the actions of the participants mirror the heroic deeds of the Celtic sagas. Dick Daly, for instance, plays a critical role in the victory of his gang by facing down the rival Morrican brothers, whose name refers to a figure with whom Cuchulain clashes on his way to the famous Battle Raid of Cooley. Here, the narrator informs us, 'was a chieftain worth deposing.' Similarly, Keane draws on a more recent oral tradition where feats of physical prowess, such as picking up a bag of cement by the teeth, were passed down through story, ballad and anecdote in the pubs of post-war London. *The Contractors*, therefore, is the product of a long tradition of myth and storytelling that helped to sustain the image of the navvy as an object of national and ethnic pride for a community that was often negatively portrayed in the British media.

Some four years later, another novel about Irish navvies in London appeared, written by Timothy O'Grady with photographs by Steve Pyke. *I Could Read the Sky* is narrated by a retired construction worker living in north London and draws upon interviews conducted by its author with elderly Irish men over a number of years. By orchestrating these accounts through multiple narrative registers into the fictionalised past of its migrant protagonist, it creates a powerful record of a disappearing heritage. Whilst it does rehearse some of the same tales of heroic masculinity found in *The Contractors*, the novel has an altogether more reflective tone which serves to create an impressionistic and somewhat haunting image of migrant displacement. The borders between fact and fiction appear to be repeatedly transgressed as the story unfolds as a series of dramatic tableaux, some of which relate to the narrator's childhood in County Clare and others to his time 'on the buildings' in post-war London.

> I open my eyes in Kentish Town. Always this neutral air. There is some grey light coming in but it hasn't that cold steely look of the winter sea I could see from the rock. A chair beside the bed. Tablets. A shirt with little blue squares, the collar shot. A bottle of Guinness here and another on the ledge. Maggie's rosary, crystal beads. The paper from home. The black box with the accordion. A bowl, spoonful of soup in it. A wardrobe made by people I've never met.

This short pithy sequence paints an archetypal picture of Irish settlement in post-war London. But its mise en scène, with the iconic trappings of national, religious and cultural identity, carry strong traces of the narrator's place of origin. References to highly specific locations in the west of Ireland—'a high rock above the house in Labasheeda' and 'the Rathangan road taking a turn in under the oaks'—periodically punctuate the text like valedictory incantations. This intensely personalised attachment to place becomes the means by which an Irish navvy, at the end of his working life in London, pays tribute to his rural inheritance and cultural identity. In contrast to *The Contractors*, this is a text that draws upon deeper traditions in Irish literature, where discourses of exile, loss, and fractured belonging are mediated through the intimate relationship between memory and imagination.

On first impressions, Edna O'Brien might seem an unlikely candidate to contribute to the genre of the 'navvy narrative'. Her portrayals of London Irish construction workers in her early novels, such as *Girls in Their Married Bliss* and

Casualties of Peace, were little more than foils for her female heroines. But as her 2006 novel, *The Light of Evening*, demonstrated, she is unrivalled by her peers when it comes to capturing the psychological and emotional ramifications of Irish migration. Her recent short story, 'Shovel Kings', is another example of this. Here, O'Brien shifts her focus from female to male experience by tracing the life of a retired Irish navvy called Rafferty. While something of the elegiac tone of *I Could Read the Sky* is apparent in this story, there are also added twists in regards to its protagonist's failed return to Ireland and his experience of exile in and between different locations of the Irish diaspora in London.

It is set in the late nineteen-nineties and opens in that most iconic location of post-war London Irish life, Biddy Mulligan's pub in Kilburn. Drinks are flowing and the wistful strains of 'The Galway Shawl' can be heard on the jukebox. We gradually get to know Rafferty as he divulges a series of accounts about his life to the unnamed female narrator of the story. For now though, as he tolerates the somewhat artificial St Patrick's Day revelries taking place in his local watering hole, his private thoughts travel back in time to the country he was forced to leave as a young man. It is not surprising, therefore, when he gets the opportunity later in the story to return to live in Ireland, that he seizes it with both hands. But Rafferty's repatriation is a disillusioning experience as he discovers the country he had cherished for so long in his memory proves to be a profoundly different place in reality. Having secured a job looking after the elderly relative of a successful building contractor, he discovers he has returned to a place he doesn't recognise anymore. Likewise, Ireland doesn't appear to recognise him either. To his dismay, he finds that nobody is interested in listening to his stories about London—stories he had looked forward to telling and had rehearsed in his mind before returning. They simply have no resonance at a time when a centuries-old experience of migration seemed to have finally come to an end with the birth of the Celtic Tiger economy.

The figure of the returnee in Irish culture has long provided the prism through which both the positive and negative aspects of Irish society have been refracted. At the opening of 'Shovel Kings', Rafferty is referred to as 'the quiet man'. In retrospect, an ironic reference, it seems, to the idealised returnee in John Ford's famous film. But rather than Sean Thornton, Rafferty's experience might be closer to that of James Bryden in George Moore's short story 'Homesickness', who returns to Ireland after thirteen years in New York. Like Bryden, Rafferty discovers that, far from fulfilling a long-cherished dream, he is now torn between two senses of home—neither of which is entirely satisfactory.

Even before he leaves for Ireland, however, Rafferty already appears to be experiencing a nostalgic longing for place—not for an idealised version of the 'auld country' he is about to return to, but rather for a particular London building site where he worked as a navvy. With evident emotion, he recalls an impromptu party that he and his workmates held at the close of a working day.

> Tears welled in his eyes as he recalled that revel, a winter evening, the glow of the fire, the leaping flames of red and blue, dancing in that London wasteland, as if in some Roman amphitheatre.

This younger and happier Rafferty might have been a character in John B. Keane's novel. His anecdotes suggest that he may well have participated in one of the many heroic feats celebrated in its pages. But we soon learn that the seeds of a very particular sense of exile were sown for Rafferty early on. When he was ordered to work on big building projects outside of London, he discovered that Camden Town, where he first arrived as a green fifteen year old, had over the years acquired the status of a surrogate homeland. Camden Town and Kilburn are prime locations in the London Irish migrant imaginary. The former had, however, lost most of the vestiges of this status by the late nineties. Perhaps, this was why Rafferty had retreated to the latter which even a decade ago was still a recognisably Irish neighbourhood.

While Rafferty is relating the final instalment of his story to the narrator, a familiar sense of displacement is once again apparent. En route back from a car-boot sale on the outskirts of London they stop off for a drink at a pub in an unfamiliar part of town. Although it is an Irish pub, it is located in a particularly run-down neighbourhood where the atmosphere is distinctly menacing. Both of them seem ill at ease. Until that is, the music starts:

> Tapping one foot, Rafferty listened, listening so intently he seemed to be hearing it there and then, and also hearing it from a great distance, rousing tunes that ushered him back to the neon purlieu of the Galtymore Dance Hall in Cricklewood.

So, on this occasion, it is Cricklewood which is subject to Rafferty's nostalgic longings. Ironic given that it's only up the road from Kilburn, the place where he had experienced a similar sense of displacement from Camden Town. Likewise, when Rafferty moves in with his girlfriend, Grania, he describes her flat as being 'many miles from Camden'. But this is Holloway, another Irish area only a stone's throw away. In other words, actual physical distance and geography appear to be irrelevant in Rafferty's experience of exile. He is caught between worlds. Not just Ireland and England, but within London he is also caught between his attachments to different Irish neighbourhoods at different times.

'The past is a foreign country,' wrote L.P. Hartley. 'They do things differently there.' For many of the navvies portrayed in post-war London Irish fiction, this would appear to be the case. But as 'Shovel Kings' closes and Rafferty prepares to leave London again, one is left with the impression that the past may indeed be the only place where he, for one, feels truly at home.

London

Feverishly, I return always running
from Ireland and built-up
yellow brick calms me
like green fields for others
and over Waterloo Bridge I go
holding on to my hat in the wind,
lights strung out on the water
the *Finnegans Wake* babble
on the 76 of 77 languages
trundling to Dalston where the Turks
are polishing their pomegranates
and Joey and myself yap through
the basement window over our mugs
of Blackstrap Molasses. This afternoon standing
in the biting cold at Mile End
my foot on the step of the red routemaster
that familiar electronic drone
announcing *277 to Highbury Corner*,
quickened me as if I'd come to a turn
in the black night, saw in a blaze
the lights of home.

Martina Evans

'Well, there was the Irish'

Clair Wills

London 1958: a couple of short vignettes. The first from a report of an Irish missionary priest, asked by the family at home in Ireland to check up on a young woman who seemed to have gone astray. The priest found the address, left his bicycle a bit down the road—priests' bikes apparently being instantly recognisable—rang the doorbell and then flattened himself against the wall of the house so those inside wouldn't see who was calling:

> The stratagem succeeded, for the door was opened by a lovely, young Irish girl. Beside her stood a little mite of perhaps three years, with a ribbon in her hair. The girl admitted that she was married in the registry.
> 'Is that little girl yours?'
> 'Yes.'
> 'What's her name?'
> 'Fatima.'
> 'That's a nice Catholic name.'
> 'Not at all; it's the name of the Prophet's daughter.'

My second scene comes from a BBC radio programme, broadcast a few weeks after the Notting Hill race riots. Much of the debate following the September 1958 riots focused on anger amongst local white youths over West Indian men taking their jobs, their unemployment benefits, and their women. The BBC interview records the conversation of a group of young men from a nearby estate in White City, where seven of the nine rioters convicted of racially aggravated violence lived. The conversation certainly reveals a good deal of insecurity amongst the youths, as it keeps circling around the issue of black men going with white girls, and Jamaican migrants getting more money and better treatment at the dole office. The group interview is full of openly racist comment: the men admit that some of them were involved in the attacks, and that they would get involved again. The following passage leads on from a discussion of the need to stop West Indians from entering the country:

> *2nd Voice*: Who is a British subject? Is a darkie a British subject, correct, an Irishman isn't, right? Now who would you sooner have in your country an Irishman or a darkie?
>
> *Voices*: An Irishman definitely.
>
> *Interviewer*: An Irishman definitely, why?
>
> *Voice*: Me old man's Irish isn't he?
>
> *2nd Voice*: Well, OK, why would you prefer an Irishman in your country, because, not because your old man's Irish, but why would you prefer an Irishman in your country to a darkie?
>
> *Voice*: Why because they're not so much scandal are they?
>
> *2nd Voice*: Not so much scandal? Well, I'll contradict you there, an Irishman can be the worst man out… He can drink (yes), fight (yes), he can run brothels, same as the darkie (yes). He can do anything.
>
> *Voice*: But they're not so bad as the darkies are they? Are you running your own country down?
>
> *2nd Voice*: No I'm not running my own country down, no no, but I've seen myself in Shepherd's Bush, in Acton, in Camden Town, in numerous parts of London, I've seen Irishmen in trouble.
>
> *Voice*: So you condemn all the blacks.
>
> *2nd Voice*: No, no, I'm not condemning the Irish or the black men. But I do believe this, I've met Englishmen that condemned the Irishmen. My name is Danny and they condemn me because I am Irish. They know my name is Danny but they won't call me Danny, they call me Pat, but when they meet a darkie they call him by his name.

The passage is fascinating because of the way the young, second-generation Irish man articulates more than he understands. His main point seems to be: it's not fair that the Irish are treated badly since we are better than West Indians, as everybody knows. But he argues this by claiming that the Irish are really just as 'bad'—'the worst man out'. Then there's that slippage between the Irish who cause trouble, and the Irish who are in trouble. The young man's confusion about where to place himself isn't edifying—what he wants is to be the same as his white mates, including in their racism, but what he articulates is his own uncertain racial designation, neither one thing nor the other.

Perhaps these two stories just tell us that people are different—that some Irish in Britain identified with other others, and some didn't, or couldn't. And there is a difference in migrant generations, of course. The young woman who has married a Muslim may be a similar age to angry, confounded Danny, but she is a new arrival. Like several others in the group of Teds, Danny's old man may be Irish, but he was born and bred in London and he feels that England is, or should be, 'my own country'. He lives in Local Authority housing in White City; he feels himself to be a rightful beneficiary of the Welfare State; houses, jobs, benefits, and even women are the wages of belonging. Fatima's mother, on the other hand, has arrived in London in the 1950s. Not quite an alien but not an insider either, she stakes her claim on the wrong side of the battle for resources. In this she is at one with the other immigrants of the 1950s, whether from the Caribbean, Cyprus, India or Pakistan—and it is an affinity she has recognised.

Urban sociologists of the fifties and sixties liked to talk about 'zones of transition', inner city areas of poor or condemned houses which were being abandoned as locals moved to new estates. New Commonwealth migrants, ineligible for the council waiting lists and turned down by mortgage companies, could buy large houses for cash and pay back their loans by letting lodgings to other newcomers, people with nowhere better to go. The Pakistani-Irish household—comprising a Pakistani landlord living alongside a mixed Asian and Irish tenantry is a staple feature of the sociology. Muhammed Anwar, writing about Rochdale in the early sixties, recounted tales of long-standing Irish girlfriends as well as more formal, instrumental relationships between landlord and tenant: 'I have three Irishmen living in one of my houses and I sometimes go and speak to them for hours as they are all single men. I get a lot of language practice like this.' John Rex and Robert Moore argued that the multiracial households they encountered in Birmingham's Sparkbrook in 1964 were parallel rather than integrated ethnic arenas, with the different races segregated within the rooms of the lodging house. There was clearly a good deal of truth to this. Single Irish men, like Irish couples with young children, were not lodging in overcrowded, condemned housing because they wanted to but because they had no choice, in the context of an acute housing shortage. The lodging houses were homes, but ones in which the relationships between inhabitants were driven by the market. One Indian landlord charged an Irish family of five £3 10s to live in one room (at a time when £2 was a lot to pay). He argued with some logic that he was doing them a favour, as they were poor people who would otherwise have to pay £7 for two rooms. Yet the stories gathered by Rex and Moore speak as much of domestic accommodation as of tension and rivalry: an Irish woman who cut through the stand-off over cleaning the communal cooker and was rewarded with chocolates by her Asian co-lodgers; the teasing of the landlord by an Irish woman who spoke to him as though he were a small child, 'to his great amusement', or another who insisted on curtseying and addressing her landlord as 'O Great King'. And then there was love and sex and marriage—accommodations of a different kind.

The idea that mixed lodgings, and mixed relationships, may have performed an important function in the social integration of immigrants was an oddly contested one during the nineteen-fifties and sixties. The assumption seems to have been that white women in relationships with Asian and Caribbean men were 'social misfits' rather than the vanguard of the future, that mixed lodgings were harbingers of disorder rather than crucibles of knowledge and experience about other people. It was at work, so the argument went, that migrants learnt to get on with the English, and vice versa. Once they left the factory, the foundry, the mill, the office or even the school they separated again into ethnic silos. It goes without saying that this theory could only be sustained if love and sex were discounted.

And there is plenty of evidence that racial segregation, as well as racial stereotyping, was rife in the fifties workplace. Aside from drinking and fighting, the principal 'trouble' associated with the Irish was of course not their brothel-keeping but their fecklessness as employees. When Pakistani men left their lodgings in Sparkbrook or Smethwick they made their way to work, principally in foundries servicing the quickly expanding car industries, where they did not encounter the Irish with whom they lived. Despite the huge demand for labour in the foundries it was almost axiomatic you would not find Irish men employed there. Or it would be more accurate to say, you would not even find the Irish. When Donall Mac Amhlaigh tried a stint in a Northampton foundry in the early fifties he found he could not bear the heat and dirt, and jacked the job in after a few days. But the reason he had got it in the first place was that no one else wanted it either. 'You can't get white people to do the menial tasks that have to be done in any foundry, not even the floating workers like the Irish.'

Like work in out-of-date mines, or unmodernised textile mills, school-leavers had no interest in the foundries when they could get work in the newer, cleaner manufacturing and light engineering industries. And until the recession of 1956-58 workers could take their pick of jobs—there was simply no need to go into dirty foundry work. Several managers interviewed at the end of the decade recalled the difficulty of hiring anybody at all:

> The big influx of immigrant labour began in 1954. At this time you couldn't get an armless, legless man, let alone an able-bodied one. Any worker could leave the works and get a job literally within three or four minutes simply by

going to the factory next door. We tried recruiting Irish labour but this didn't come off. The Manager went over to Ireland himself and recruited 36 men. Of these, only 8 actually turned up at the works, and only one stayed for any length of time.

The first foreign labour we employed were German and Italian prisoners of war. When these men were repatriated, the firm found itself short of labour. Poles were employed and a number still work here. They were very good workers, but we couldn't get enough to make up for the labour shortage. The Ministry of Labour had coloured people. We wouldn't look at them at first, but eventually we succumbed. It was a case of necessity: there was no one else. Well, there was the Irish, but they were dreadful. Only about one in twenty was any good.

It was this kind of foundry which Peter Wright spent six weeks observing for the Institute of Race Relations in 1961, in order to write a report on racial integration in the workplace. The status of foundry work had steadily declined since the high point of the hungry 1930s when, 'it was almost impossible to get a job here; you practically had to wait for someone to die before you could get in.' In 1953 the 'newcomer' element in the workforce amounted to one Italian (an ex-prisoner-of-war) and one Pakistani. But by 1962, 75% of the workforce were from Asia and the Caribbean, and they were mainly doing unskilled, physically demanding jobs. Knocking out and quenching of castings, for example: 'Neither job is relished by the white workers. Knocking out is a sledge-hammer job. It's outside work, so it's cold in winter and in summer the bits of sand stick to you when you're sweating.' Or electrode cleaning: 'This is the sort of job that if a white man took it, he doesn't really want a job at all. The West Indians are mainly employed on scrap-crushing. A sledge hammer job. They also do the loading and unloading of pitch. The highest job done by any coloured worker is fork-lift truck operator.'

A gloss, therefore, on the ubiquitous complaints against the Irish for their unreliability. The Irish appear to have been 'dreadful' insofar as they insisted they were 'white'—insofar as they were not prepared to take the jobs that other white workers felt were beneath them, jobs that were so demeaning that to do them meant you didn't 'really want a job at all'. Like Mac Amhlaigh they packed their bags, and they were not offered the jobs that the white English (as opposed to Germans, Italians and Poles) thought were theirs. Irish fecklessness and unreliability, then, was partly the flip-side of Irish pride. It was the trouble with being neither one thing nor the other—a trouble which, despite their differences, both Danny and the mother of little Fatima understood.

Death trap for beauty

i.m. Matthew

All day spent edging
the grass in Kensington.
Now you strut naked,
except for the Claddagh,
show bum and tanned pecs
to the mirror.

Most evenings we'd be
monosyllabic; just mephitic wind
from the dog or rainwater
plinking into the Harrods tin.
But tonight we take a vein
to the cinema

watch something beautiful
unravel in darkness.
Two seats in a cemetery—
you stuffing popcorn
next to a coinín
with myxomatosis.

Michael Ray

Les Papillons De Belsize

Patrick McCabe

Unawed history may consider comment superfluous upon the ultimate destination point of these impertinent times, and in particular the current disposition and likely future fortunes of the city-state English capital— with its hardly less than reasonable position perhaps being that Olympian correspondents such as Messrs. T. S. Eliot, Raymond Williams and George Orwell have already more than distinguished themselves in this regard.

But putative assessors may well one day come upon this humble account of my own, one effectively commissioned by a very dear friend and neighbour. That is to say a certain Mrs Peter Hughie Carberry in the year 1971. When, upon learning that my 'taking the boat across' was imminent, prevailed upon me not to hesitate before 'dropping her a wee line', in the time-honoured tradition of so many of my countrymen. Most notably, as she reminded me, the Inspector of Drains from the County Leitrim, the water-colourist and popular songwriter known as Percy French, whose 'Emigrant's Letter' tune remained so memorable and dear to her heart, she informed me, before clearing her throat and beginning, somewhat extravagantly, to pipe: *Dear Danny I'm takin' the pen in my hand / To tell you we're just out of sight of the land…*

Before I hastily made my goodbyes and clambered aboard the bus that was set to take me to Dublin and the North Wall, hence to Soho, and, hopefully, the wilful embrace of unethical hedonism and untamed bouts of heretofore unprecedented indulgence and dissolution.

What could possibly be in store for me, I kept wondering as we passed through those townlands which I never would see again—Drumhowan, Drung and the scarcely pronounceable Tullynahinera. Yes, as the hedgerows and ditches of County Monaghan sped past in the morning sun, I reflected, like the man with the wheelbarrow, it was all before me now.

'Just make sure now and don't forget!' I remembered Mrs Peter admonishing, 'Like Percy French! Your Emigrant's Letter now, do you hear me, Wee Pat?'

Wee Pat certainly would not indeed, he said to himself. As he tapped his trusty notebook secreted deep in the confines of his inside pocket. That would be the very first task on my list. Mrs P. had spent the war years as a staff nurse in St Mary's Hospital, Paddington. And indeed had recalled those days fondly for me as we stood there chatting. 'How could I ever have been such an eejit?' she had snarled unexpectedly, as I gulped there beside her with my hands in my pockets, before stroking my chin as was my fashion in those faraway days, after the manner of some diminutive and excessively scholarly cleric.

'All I can say is that I must have been on drugs to have ever considered leaving that delightful principality!' she had continued acidly, 'where I could have myself a nice cuppa tea and a penny bun in Lyons Corner House not to mention a nice mannerly soldier to compliment me on my dancing. It's a pity Hitler didn't come over here and blow this bloody place out of it! '

Harsh words indeed, I reflected as the bus left the townland of Aghadrumaginshaheera far behind. I resumed my preoccupied psychological peregrinations, rapt in renewed considerations of the British Empire induced by my neighbour's wistful reminiscence of those legendary tea rooms on The Strand.

How remote from my experience and yet how vivid, I was thinking—as I too shook my head, ponderously considering the somewhat unfortunate and deeply unpleasant nature of my recent departure from the town of my birth. Where, subsequent to my engagement with my genial gardening neighbour, I had found myself waylaid by a number of former 'comrades', one might say, who had stood between me and the bus, with their solid phalanx forming an ominous shadow.

'Hippyhead McCabe! Stop right there when you're tault!,' barked Patsy Donohoe, what's all this we've been hearing about you going to London?

'I've got a job as a window cleaner!,' I explained, 'in Shoreditch!'

I shall never forget the response with which my hastily cobbled rationale was received. As Patsy, a youth of my own age but of immensely greater bulk, laced up a fierce-looking hobnailed boot with dark intent, before turning to face his associates, parting his hands in disconsolate imprecation.

Let the tragedy which ensued be swiftly redacted.

'All that's over there is protestants and darkies! So you needn't be thinking of coming back here!'

It was a bitter lesson.

But as I sat down that evening to pen my letter to Mrs Peter regarding my experiences, the resentments it had incurred were already happily beginning to fade. Thanks not so much to one's own interior discipline or commodious reserves of human empathy but, if the truth be told, to the ingestion of a number of stimulants concomitant with its composition which had just been provided by my host, 'Big Tommy Mc Larnon', custodian of the 'squat' in which I'd just arrived. 'Ah Mrs Peter!' I sighed as my eyes began melting, 'How cool to be able to write to you, babesters!'

As I set to once more, clutching my broken biro, also provided by 'mine host'.

13 Melrose Avenue
Willesden
March 27 1971
Dear Danny I'm taking the pen in my hand! Yeah, I sure am, Mrs Peter!
Just like I promised, Goddamnit! Already things are looking good.
I'll be starting cleaning windows tomorrow! …

What was the impulse that drove me so passionately towards that great city in those days?

Certain indications can be derived from what survives of that ragged document, my emigrant's letter with its elaborate embroidery of Robert Crumb-style cartoon images. Along with numerous, somewhat primitive renderings of the of the world-famous Roundhouse, that magnificent structure at the edge of the Chalk Farm earthworks where even still, right to this very day, you can hear them yet. By which I mean the spectral ululations of hordes of men and horses, with masses of wood and metal everywhere—which was, it would appear, at least to some extent responsible for my ineradicable longing to get away and live in London. Because, you see, that little County Monaghan town had once been a major railway junction, and there had existed there an equally glorious circular engine shed, constructed in the architectural style so favoured by mid-Victorian bankers, possessed of a massive dignity and inspired confidence. With its boardrooms and white marble fireplaces, not to mention its Victorian fenders, coal scuttles and clocks wreathed in laurel. And where, as you stood on its steps between slender columns of cast iron filled with glass, staring out over the roofs of the old platform sheds, you might easily have been floating aloft with the starlings, wheeling in a smoky London sunset, as side-whiskered men in corduroy conversed animatedly with engine-drivers in stove-pipe hats. Day after day I would make it my business to gaze upon it, with its frozen music nonpareil—yes, almost identical to the London one, yes The Roundhouse, dating from 1847 and designed by Stephenson, originally a house for locomotives travelling north.

It was also the case that, in a manner not dissimilar to that of the 'freaks' who at that time had begun to haunt Chalk Farm and Camden Town, there had always been something proprietorial about my personal relationship with the Clones Roundhouse. And maybe that's the reason that I began to perceive myself entitled to institute a series of what might be described as 'apprentice nonconformist gatherings' for some months prior to my eventual departure. A type of 'psychedelic crusade' was seen to ensue, which in no way had endeared me to Patsy Donohoe and Co.—who took exception to our communal perusal of *International Times*, as well as the periodicals *Sounds* and *NME* and *Melody Maker* too. 'Dream on, mothers, you ain't got a prayer!' they might overhear us say whenever they happened to be sauntering past. As we flicked imaginary joints in their wake. Unfortunately, as a consequence, on a number of occasions being cruelly apprehended—and beaten up.

Yes, that was the type of thing that went on in those days, as we assembled nightly in our own private Roundhouse. Because that of course was the type of talk which you heard from the hippies over in London—when they weren't passing around little pipes of 'blow'. And which hopefully explains the somewhat peculiar and idiosyncratic tone of the 'epistle' I dispatched the following morning to Mrs Peter—marked 'The Emigrant's Letter' in gigantic bubble writing. And which included a great many phrases with which, likely as not, she would have been unfamiliar—including 'too much', 'It's a gas!', 'Way out', and 'Smashed'. Along with random, and at times quite inexplicable references to 'Black Unity', 'Gay Liberation', and 'International Marxist Groupings'.

Yes, I thought as I posted my envelope (sans the actual letter, as it later transpired), how far away did my hometown already seem. Becoming wistful just like Percy French must have done, only in my case not for old wooden gates and soporific cows in uneventful summer meadows but for some of the imaginary concerts our Clones Collective had mounted. Particularly memorable, I remember recalling, had been the set Syd Barrett and Pink Floyd had played upon one otherwise quite unremarkable Saturday afternoon. But even that was surpassed by the appearance of The Crazy World Of Arthur Brown.

With the actual truth—yes, now it can can be told!—being that Arthur Brown and 'The Floyd' had never been anywhere Clones or its so-called Roundhouse. But that didn't stop us organising further 'iconoclastic engagements', and along with them a variety of unrehearsed 'anti-narrative' dramas, as well as staged interviews with Tariq Ali and Abbie Hoffmann.

'I'm heading down The King's Road,' I used to say, putting on an English accent—before sauntering off heedlessly, as if trying to throw 'the Fuzz' off the scent.

And which, as I say, perhaps goes some little way to explaining the wanton, counter-cultural tone of my haplessly undelivered letter to Mrs Peter.

With it only really dawning on me the following day, in the aftermath of some twelve or thirteen more joints of superior Pakistani Black that my 'free jazz' approach to letter-writing might not, in any case, have been greatly appreciated by Mrs Peter, however cosmopolitan and liberal her London experiences might have rendered her. To be honest it read like an Arts Lab performance poem more than a homage to the deceased Inspector of Drains.

How innocent it seems with the passing of the years!

Hey Mrs P! So then—what's shakin'? How in the hell are Tommy McGurran's hens?

The letter, if memory serves, had also included a description of a tube ride to Hackney. But mostly it consisted of a string of fingerprints and ink blots. I can still remember that East London visit, though—and that august borough, with its magnificent cathedral of variety The Hackney Empire, decorated in that curious compound of Renaissance motifs that can only be described as late Victorian, and which appear in office blocks, pubs and banks all over London. Ever since I read 'The Blitz Kid' in *The Dandy*, I would dream of wandering in the bombed-out interiors of those echoing amphitheatres, where mirrors reflected striped wallpaper and gas lights, gorging on the baroque in those empty plum-velvet plush seats.

Ciao babes! I'll drop you another line next week! I signed off to Mrs Peter.

Before heading to the Scala in King's Cross for its weekly all-niter. *The Corpse-Grinders* was showing in tandem with *Sssss*.

That's a movie about a man-snake.

'Why are there no barrage balloons in this town?' I used to ask my father at the age of four or five. 'Or signs that say "frying tonight" outside the stupid chip shop?'

There weren't even coppers who looked liked PC Plod.

'It's to do with De Valera,' my father explained as best he could—before grinning like Korky as he sighed in his chair and said that Dev was the boy that put it up to them. 'He soon softened Winston Churchill's cough!'

Such pleasure as the London of *The Dandy* used to give me! No wonder I drew a picture of Korky the Cat for Mrs Peter! Yes, and also pleasures untold to be gleaned from those other repositories of wonder, those stark and grey cine-reels experienced in so many Odeons at that time. That is to say those *Scales Of Justice* movies made in Merton Park, depicting that liquorice-black world of Scotland Yard in the 1950s, all of them starring the sepulchral Edgar Lustgarten. In the city of 'The Blitz Kid', with no end of roasted chestnuts and cockney sparrers, and with the barrage balloons only recently taken down.

'Have you ever murdered anyone?' whispers Edgar, tenting his fingers. 'Or perhaps you'd rather not say?'

Well, certainly not, Edgar, to a detective who routinely—not to say brazenly—made things up.

But then—who doesn't? For, as I'm sure you've already gathered, there isn't, and wasn't, and never will be any 'emigrant's letter', to Mrs Peter, or anyone else.

And which is why my London is one which might be said to exist somewhere in the Twilight Zone of memory and reinvention, perhaps between a documentary shot in formal ashen shades and glistening blacks, at once stripped of colour, reimagined in form and line, in contrast and shadow—grey and wintry stark black and white but simultaneously shot through with acidic streaks of yellow and green. With the whole comprising a cine-poem with jerky and discontinuous editing rhythms, an impertinent fiction which exists solely to give me pleasure. And maybe with a bit of luck, a reader or two.

Yes, a fictive city in other words, whose soundtrack might have been scored by Les Reed and Barry Mason, and shot by Alain Resnais with a little assistance from Alain Robbe-Grillet, as memory's wintry archive reel material and its reportage look assumes the melted crayon motley hue of literary deceit and blatant reinvention.

Along the same lines as Mrs Peter's 'emigrant letter'. And in which I cast myself as the star of so many Londons—cities as yet which had to be experienced, maybe never even would, seeing as largely they didn't exist. Among them, even, a sad little seventeen-year-old window cleaner, singing his heart out as he wobbles along on an imaginary bicycle, serenading a panoply of 'posh birds', as all along The Strand, and outside Lyon's Corner House, an impish fictional Margate-style band surge in a sympathetic swell of tumescence.

Yes, back in those days I could just as readily have become the star of the not-Fellini masterpiece *Confessions Of A Window Cleaner*—bleating defiantly, swerving and pedalling through a world that could only have ever been in a delicious commingling of the hometown of my imagination, and another favourite movie of the period, a musical dream-short without words entitled *Les Bicyclettes De Belsize*.

Which is how I will always chose to remember the city in those innocent days, bright and uplifting in spite of all the rain—with a soundtrack provided by what Bob Stanley has described as the seaside brass sound of sunset yellow, London's own indigenous brand of bubblegum, carefree and indomitable.

And the memory of which prompted me, once and for all, to recommence my imaginary letter to Mrs Peter, now counted along with Jerry Garcia among the growing ranks of the, hopefully, 'Grateful' Dead. Except this time finishing it, as I sit here with my laptop (laptop!) in a corner of a pub in Belsize Road, ruminating upon Marx and the psychotropic properties of Pakistani Black, and anarchic philosophies about as remote now as gas jets and walrus moustaches.

And thinking of the opening of that movie and the impossibly beautiful morning it had photographed, with its starlings leaping as the camera tracked slowly along rooftop eaves before steadily fixing its lens on me, and the absurdly optimistic world of youth I'd once inhabited.

With my thoughts being played as though on minor chords on the barrel organ of memory and imagination, modulating into a great waltz that mimicked the trajectory of a dizzying Red Admiral which went sailing past the window before finally swerving towards the Kilburn High Road, where so often I'd defiantly fist-bumped the future, pledging allegiance to no end of improbable causes, from all of which I have long since been exiled.

But for one, that of art which remains obstinately enduring, and to which I pen this little missive in acknowledgement of both it and its handmaiden, memory—whose sustaining power, and curiously bashful relationship with creativity has proved inestimable, and oftentimes as beautiful and infinitesimal as the quiet of London's suburban streets on a Sunday morning, or a snatch of florid strings from a semi-open window, soaring before fading, like a pertinacious coloured butterfly hanging high above Belsize.

Those London Visits

Evelyn Conlon

An unexpected thing happened last year which catapulted me right back to the nineteen-eighties—a place that I don't mind revisiting at all, despite the apparently gloomier recession, not to mention the price of an Aer Lingus ticket to anywhere, with no other carrier off the island. It was also a time of almost laughably dark social laws that we had to fight morning, noon and particularly night. On top of that, the waiting list to have a phone installed could stretch to seven years. We had no landline distinction then: a phone was a phone. It would nearly make you stay in a bad marriage not to have to go out to the coinbox on the road. But oh how lovely it was to get on the boat and not to be contactable, pure heaven, total freedom, mind-enhancing silence, a space to get up to all sorts of thoughts and things in limbo land between one island and the other. And of course the visit to the bank and the queue to change punts into sterling at the Foreign Exchange counter added seriousness and grandeur to the journey. This was before boxes in the wall with money in them, before e-mail, before having to listen to the fan of pointlessness on mobile phones, before laptops, I kid you not, and here's me still alive and dancing.

What happened was that I walked into a Liverpool bookshop called News from Nowhere and the last thirty years vanished into thin air. I was suddenly back to my stolen visits to London in the early eighties, one of which was undertaken in pursuit of a terrific opportunity to get me a new life. I won't go into the personal circumstances that made this essential, I only do that in the rooms of friends who are versed in the rules of privacy.

It isn't pointless remembering that drives me to write about this, although I know that one person's nostalgia can be another person's golden moment of revelation. What makes me think about it is that it is sometimes crucial to look at what we have almost lost, so that perhaps we can retrieve it, just in time. By that I mean the independent bookshop as meeting place, as metre of our lives, as our fresh air. Outside on the street people were edgy with talk, but in News from Nowhere everything fell away. The irregular arrangement of the shelves gave a maze-like quality to the browsing. The expressed murmurous delight at finding a treasure could not be exactly pinpointed; the stands resting at irregular angles gave the entire experience a tinge of Hundertwasser. It brought back all the bookshops of that time, among them Well Read, our own Books Upstairs, and my first port of call in London, Sisterwrite.

Sisterwrite, located at 190 Upper Street in Islington, was an unapologetic feminist bookshop. And no, it's not true that they didn't allow men, but it is true that, certainly in the beginning, not many men went there. And before the howls of exclusion go up, let me explain that we understood the necessity of dedicated areas of study, and boy was that what was going on then. And anyway the men weren't interested in what we were reading. Yet. Each one of us women peering starry-eyed at the titles had spent the previous hundred years, it seemed, reading books that had often left us first uneasy, then furious with longing for descriptions that made sense to us. We had reached the end of our tethers being inaccurately, patronisingly imagined.

Obviously, Sisterwrite sold books by women, but not just titles published by Virago or The Women's Press. It was full of fascinatingly obscure imports and radical magazines that dealt with things you never knew that you didn't know. The politics were serious but not gloomy. Much of the work on display was about new definitions, an amazing amount of it about Sexuality. And Love and Longing. And Racism. How we had to learn. I should say that I wasn't a complete innocent in any or all of this. I had already worked in the Miners' Bar in the Australian desert, poured pints for wandering men, and done some community work down on the dry river bed where many Aborigines made their home. But Sisterwrite and its cousins gave us something else, it wasn't about reading what we agreed with—often, in fact, it was about what we profoundly didn't agree with, or were heretofore ignorant of: 'I'll buy that just to show how much better my thinking processes are'. It was with that in mind that I bought Andrea Dworkin's *Right Wing Women,* and learned explanations that still stand to me. The experience of those bookshops was more about challenging than placating. We knew we were going against the cultural grain but once our feet went over the door we were in a sort of home. And as a fledgling writer I was finding the consolation of seeing work that had its eyes wide open.

If it was the polemical writing that drew me in, it was the fiction that got me. I was attempting a race away from the established myopic view of Irish lives—this would include blasphemous things like women actually thinking for themselves, not simply reacting to what mostly men writers insisted they thought. And also flying a bit further than had already been done by the few women allowed past the bouncers. The politics of course were reassuring, and sometimes amusing, but to be honest, it was easy to split my desires. It was in the Fiction corner that I proceeded to lose time.

It might be an interesting, if difficult, thing to match stories with those buying adventures, but although the events are clear in the mind I'm not sure how accurate the timelines would be. In the collision of memories—a massive pile-up—I suddenly remember picking up a book for a prisoner whom I was visiting. She was an English anarchist who had once wanted to be a rally driver. I was doing Crime and Deviance in my Sociology Studies. The reason I had been asked to visit her was because of things I had written. But when I went to see her in Mountjoy Prison I was too embarrassed (or was it too afraid?) to talk about poetry and short stories. When she finally got out she wasted no time in letting me know how disappointed she had been that I wouldn't talk about what I was working on. And she had been afraid to ask, because maybe I wasn't writing at all.

I remember once seeking refuge in the bookshop after a shockingly violent event when a BNP gang had swept through an alternative Finsbury Park type fleadh. The people there, the cut of their clothes, the food they ate, the magazines they sold, the hairstyles, the people they mixed with, their tolerances, the sight of their huggings, all drove the local lodge of racists totally mad. It's the sound of the first person being hit that I remember most, the crack of fist on face, and then the hurricane-like destruction of the stalls.

Another time I left Sisterwrite, as usual delighted by my purchases, and perhaps being a bit dreamy about that and the escape route from my life that I was working out, still, I walked across the street not seeing a speeding car roaring towards me. It clipped me and sent me flying, along the footpath, luckily, instead of under its wheels. In the process of relocating my brain's place in the outside world I had managed to become a hit and run statistic. Weirdly, I wouldn't allow anyone to help me, but managed to get to where I was staying and was asked by an occupant of the place what star sign I was—apparently she had a remedy for Scorpios in shock. Actually she had a remedy for anyone in shock, but more of the one for Scorpios, wasn't I lucky? As soon as she had administered this, and left me alone, I got to Euston as fast as I could and left the escape route for another time.

In thinking about those bookshop visits—those lifelines—I believe that, as readers, we took across the thresholds with us an almost overwhelming desire not just for the naming of our puzzlement but for a total restructuring of the very questions themselves. We needed bookshops that reflected our hungers. We needed the conferral of acceptance on our voracious burrowing out, our quite savage kicking aside of walls that we felt had hemmed us in. We were of the generation who had sat fuming in classrooms at our exclusions. Well, actually, we had had the nerve to bring up the word and had rather liked the possibilities that the discussion offered. And this was re-education at its most basic level, being taken on voluntarily and becoming the basis of what we believed would be a more equal, and therefore more interesting, world. The books we sought and found were astonishing in that they pushed out all the limits. They most certainly did not have blue, pink, or pastel covers! (There's a bookshop close to me and I have to put the scarf up over my eyes when I pass it.)

So you may be wondering what 'loss' I am warning about. My fear is that we're in danger of losing the challenge of those establishments. What happens now is that the window can be bought and all the exciting, innovative work has been bulldozed by giddy marketing. Too many people now make straight for the prize-winning shelf. I am not averse to the notion of the occasional prize, and yes I understand that it is a method of bringing attention to the as yet unknown, but when the bookshop experience seems like you've been tipped into a tombola then clearly we have lost sight of the art of finding our own books.

I know that discussing the present hurricane of prizes may seem like a hefty jump from walking into a bookshop—but I think not. I am of course seriously aware that this is a very tricky area for a writer to touch—we don't do it because we are afraid of being accused of having sour grapes. But I'll chance it, because far too many of us are being silenced by this tyranny and are afraid to be counted as skeptics. I see the over-emphasis of prizes as the devaluation of all those wonderful mysteries we were out looking for. For all that hope flying in on wings. For the expectation that we would have to search for a book that might satisfy our particular curiosities. Now there seems to be a conspiracy to have us all reading the same book at the same time. What could be more awful, more anathema to a non-school-goer's right to life? Leaving aside the fact that, yes, a prize listing has become the new black—think for a moment that a multinational publishing company has control over what is even allowed to be entered, never mind what makes it for consideration. Of course the occasional maverick gets through, the occasional voice that adds a special light to the way you fit yourself in the world, but surely we must be suspicious of the narrowing consensus of what makes a good work? Suspicious of those who decide talent on marketability and on how 'palatable' we can make a real story. In that past era of ferocious questioning we were thoroughly exercised by who got to decide the canon. We were going to change it, forever. And we did in some ways, but unfortunately we merely handed it over to a different set of the same faces, this time including the prize givers. I have recently heard of a book being given a prize because it had been given a prize. When Ben Okri takes it on himself to advise African writers about how to make it, he may be doing so with a heavy heart. He may be suggesting a narrowing of the view to what will pass the boardroom and the new gatekeeper, who turns out to have not dissimilar tactics to the old. 'It doesn't sing for us,' I was recently told, about a book I had just enjoyed. 'I should sincerely hope not,' I said, 'it's a book, not a canary.'

At the risk of sounding like a creaking fossil, I suggest that in the 1980s you didn't buy a book because it was on *The X Factor*; you picked it by what was written on the back of it, and if you were fascinated by the time you'd finished reading it, you told someone else. Just in case you think that was all plain sailing, don't get me wrong, you could make a mistake. I was once so taken by a back cover and a first page that I bought the book as a present for several people. I still cringe, because I cannot remember exactly who they are, so there are people out there who think I agree with the politics in that dreadful book that I shall not name. And yet I'll have to admit that there's a kind of freedom in buying a book just because there's something on the back of it that you don't understand, or disagree with.

What Sisterwrite and those related bookshops were about was getting varying views, not being corralled into reading one book because it has had bestowed upon it, not one, but all the prizes that year. This is a worldwide problem. The Australian novelist, David Foster, bravely brought it up when he was accepting a prize himself, the Patrick White Literary Award, the honour that White set up with his Nobel prize money specifically for authors who have made a significant, but inadequately-recognised, contribution to Australian literature. Or, as Foster put it: 'a kind of literary loser's compo'. He also went on to take a swipe at another, unnamed, writer (clearly J.M. Coetzee) for putting 'his hand up for every prize, including—can you believe it?—the Randwick Council Literature Award' despite having a Nobel and two Booker prizes. I bring this up because I am increasingly saddened for the apprentice writers who think that the only way their work can be judged is by a prize listing. I've been in rooms where younger writers don't think they're alive if they're not on some list. How terrible. And what an awful thing for the industry to be subjecting writers to. As if it wasn't hard enough to do the work, then to have yourself entered into a ring against your colleagues.

Fay Weldon once remarked that prize ceremonies were not so much about rewarding the chosen winner but more about watching the cheque being snatched away from the others on the list. Surely this is not what a writing life should be about. And let's make something else clear that pertains to Irish writers. It is not true that the many large prizes are open to Irish writers as is always claimed. They cannot be entered for any of the prizes that take place in Britain unless they are published by a British publisher. And not everyone is going to be published in England, why would they be? Also clearly there is a certain type of Irish literature which will never be published there. Naturally. Now, wouldn't it be an interesting boost to the Irish publishing industry if the Impac prize was only open to books published in Ireland? How that would change the landscape of what is lauded as representing us. Yes, I am sometimes filled with despair standing in front of a group of beginning writers who ask me about prizes. Should I tell them that if they are aiming to live a life on tenterhooks they might just be better taking up playing poker machines?

I found David Foster's postal address and wrote him a card, congratulating him on the nerve, and he wrote back thanking me. Apparently this was not the reaction that had greeted him in the media. Our communication over the matter was heartening, but, you know, you can have such a thing as a sad dance.

Nostalgia can have its uses. Sisterwrite is long gone, as is its offspring Silver Moon. But News from Nowhere is still in Liverpool and Books Upstairs is still in Dublin (and has expanded in fact—there's 'flying in the face'). And in London there's The Stoke Newington Book Shop, the Big Green Bookshop, and I hope more that I don't know. And I have remembered why we need to get into them. If you've ever looked up at the swishing sound a flock of birds makes you will know that it leaves a freedom in its wake. It brush-strokes the air around you. Diving into proper bookshops can do that too.

Photograph: John Minihan

Days of the Lamb
Matthew Sweeney

Strange as it seems now, I lived in London for almost thirty years—from the mid-seventies until the beginning of the current century. For most of that time I lived right in the centre, in Holborn, on a small strip of road called Dombey Street (renamed after the Dickens novel at the end of the war) which joins the bigger, trendier Lamb's Conduit Street, at the end of which is the elegant pub, The Lamb. Outside this hangs a sign, depicting a lamb, and there are stained-glass pictures of lambs on the windows. Inside, it retains its old-style design, with little swinging snob windows all the way round the bar (so the posh gentlemen wouldn't have to look at the minions serving them their pints of ale), and not a cheep is even yet to be heard from a television or a jukebox or any piped music system. Conversation still rules here, and it's quite an art to find a seat on a Friday evening.

The reader can imagine the pleasure of having such a pub as one's local, and indeed I was often to be found there, as I was much more partial to beer back then than I am now. I used to even slip down there to scribble in my notebook, aware that the pub had a very special literary heritage, for Dickens had drunk there in the nineteenth century, and it was there in the late fifties, that Ted Hughes had courted Sylvia Plath. As Plath was my poetry goddess, and I was quite partial to Hughes as well, I hoped that some of their magic might rub off on me. I spent so much time there in a little snug that one day when a friend found me in situ, Rosemary, the wife of the publican, announced that Matthew was in his office. She was an English lady, and her husband, Richard, was from Northern Ireland, and they were both very tall. They had a very tall dog, too—a gentle giant of a wolfhound which was possibly named Rory. Anyway, they seemed happy enough to accommodate my scribbling, and were well aware of the Hughes/Plath story.

By that stage, the mid-eighties, I was embarked on my publication career, with a couple of books out. I was also attending a poetry group that met every month or so in Notting Hill Gate, at the home of the Derry-born poet Robert Greacen, who had not so long before published a collection with Gallery Press, *A Garland for Captain Fox*, that had caught my attention. Robert's first publications had been during the Second World War, so it was safe to call his recent publication a renaissance. Anyway, I went along to Pembridge Crescent every month, clutching my bottle of cider, which was the entry requirement, as well as the obligatory new poem to be chewed over. It is safe to say that the standard of poetry at that group was variable. There were some published poets, and some not so published—one elderly chap whose only claim to fame was that he'd published a poem in *The New Statesman* in the 1950s. I will not name any of the people who attended that group, I will just mention that one always wanted the poet who was the fiercest critic there to sum up one's poem as 'A splendid piece!', as he was known to occasionally do, although I remember his comment to *The New Statesman* contributor once that the poem just shared with us was the worst poem the critic had ever read in his life.

Robert had been earning his living teaching adult education classes and when he retired he moved to Dublin to avail of Aosdána's Cnuas, so that was the end of the Pembridge Poets. After a decent length of time I decided to form another poetry group, inviting a few of the earlier group but a lot more who might be called the poets who were emerging just then. I'm talking about people like Jo Shapcott, Michael Donaghy, Don Patterson, Lavinia Greenlaw, Eva Saltzman, Sarah Maguire, Ruth Padel, Maurice Riordan, Tim Dooley, and I'm not going to run through everyone who attended. Besides, people didn't always show up. To begin with we met in my flat in Dombey Street—we opted for Saturday afternoons, rather than the evening meetings of the earlier group. We tended to meet slightly less often, nearer every two months, than monthly. I instigated further changes as well—I decided that the poems would be presented anonymously, so in theory no one would know whose poem was under discussion (often, of course, one would know or think one knew). I'd nominate someone to read the poem out loud, and I'd hand out photocopies to everyone. Having calculated how much time we had for each poem (which depended on how many poems had been brought—often people brought none), I'd appoint someone as timekeeper whose job it was to indicate when the discussion time was up by making a loud noise appropriate to the poem we were looking at.

As can be imagined, the standard of poetry brought to this group was usually pretty high, and the level of criticism tended to be searching. The drink of the afternoon was wine (which my daughter Nico, then twelve or thirteen, took delight in distributing), rather than the cider of the Notting Hill sessions, and one hoped one's poem would come under discussion earlier rather than later. I remember a funny incident happening during one of the workshops. Four poems had been looked at, and were unusually good, and I distributed the photocopies of a fifth to the participants. Ruth Padel had brought her dog, Jenny (a labradoodle), and I left a copy of each poem under the dog's nose. For the first four poems the dog had made no sound. This fifth poem, however, was a different kettle of fish—none of us knew how to begin commenting on it. The dog started growling, then got to its feet and started barking at the poem, and I announced that the dog had good taste, whereupon the knives started coming down on the poem, as they came down on Banquo in Act III Scene III of *Macbeth*.

It was, I admit, a bit disruptive of family life to have the flat taken over for four hours or so on a Saturday afternoon. As well as my daughter, my son Malvin, two years younger, was also in the picture. After three or four workshops I began trying to think of an alternative meeting place. Some of us must have been talking about this in the Lamb afterwards—we tended to repair there following the workshop, to celebrate or lick our wounds—and the conversation was overheard by Richard, the landlord. To my delight he informed us he had a large room upstairs, and he would be more than happy to let us borrow it for four hours on the occasional Saturday afternoon. Thus was born the Lamb Poetry Group.

It was the perfect solution. We would meet around 1.30, have a drink, and take another upstairs to begin the workshop at 2. We'd have a drink-pause halfway through, and would bring the session to a close at 6pm. At the beginning of the first Lamb meeting the wolfhound Rory came into the room, put his front paws on the table and looked around the group, as if wishing us and our poems well. We needed the dog's good wishes. Sometimes one would bring a poem along thinking it was all right, but would take it away knowing a lot more work needed to be done. This was all to the good, of course, and an excellent experience for an emerging poet. It is fair to say, however, that not every attender came looking for suggestions to improve their poem. Michael Donaghy, for example, once told me he'd never changed a single word of any poem he'd brought to the group.

We occasionally had visitors from outside. Usually it was other poets (I remember Kit Wright coming once with a poem urging people to beware of a man in black) but not always. Once, Greg Gatenby, the organiser of Toronto's Harborfront Festival, dropped in—he'd heard of the group. As it happened, the first poem up that afternoon was one of mine, from a new venture of writing poems for children, and as such, quite different to my normal stuff. So safe in the extra anonymity, I proceeded to criticise the poem strongly, causing other people to defend it. Afterwards, Gatenby came for a drink with us. 'Jeez,' he said, 'Are you guys always as tough as that on each other?'

That wasn't the only example of people outside the country hearing about the group. One day I was contacted by a Mexican poet who was in town and wanted to meet with me and some of the others. I rang Donaghy and he came round to Dombey Street, where we were joined by two Mexican poets, Pedro Serrano and Carlos Lopez Beltran. Over a bottle of wine the Mexicans told us they wanted to edit a poetry anthology called *The Lamb Generation*. In time, this came out, and six poets flew out to Mexico to the launch, three from the Lamb group but three others who had nothing to do with it. Still, the name stuck.

There's an old cliché that all good things comes to an end, and so it was with the Lamb workshop. We'd had two years, or maybe three. I felt it had run its course—none of us were emerging now, we had our own distinct voices, our strong likes and dislikes, and the general tenor of the discussions wasn't as open to difference anymore. I discussed it with the others, some agreed with me, some wanted the group to go on. It didn't, although I heard later there were a couple of spin-off groups. I even visited one once when I had a poem I didn't know how to end, but I was appalled to find a level of bad-tempered disagreement such as never had been encountered in the Lamb workshop. It put me in mind of opposing football fans at a derby match. I never went to a poetry group again.

A Zoology of London

Wildlife lies behind the land
like seventeenth-century wallpaper

behind Edwardian parlour print
behind a buff matt finish.

Infant elephant ears poke up
the pavement. Shark gills ripple

as wind slashes the polythene
of a puddle. Eyes flash on

Victorian brick owls when
the Top Floor Flat gets home first

on the kind of winter nights that
make sardines push doors into

square whales to hear opera in fabric
ribs washed up on the South Bank.

This is all the world coming together,
joining zoology to architecture

to history to paper:
right here, right now.

And here is all the world falling
away again, its wall as heavy as

the mammoths still pounding
the sedge beneath your feet.

Sarah Barnsley

Ghastly

Gavin Corbett

Our local library was like something out of Germany, that's what everyone used to say; and that summer when I was twelve, and I had started to find the macabre in everything, I looked at the library's witchy cupola and steep-pitched Bavarian red-tiled roof and I thought of eagles' nests and wolves' lairs and mass murder. It had only a small range of books—it was a bulky building; so bulky its insides seemed squeezed—and too many of the books were fiction, which I had no interest in. Still more were about nursing, strangely, and gardening and car maintenance—something for every contented resident of the district of Foxrock and Cabinteely. And then I found something for me: 'Omits absolutely none of the gruesome details,' the cover promised. It was *The Complete Jack the Ripper* by Donald Rumbelow, and I was to take it out on repeat loan for the next few months.

The facts of the case were easy to memorise because I was so quickly engrossed. I learnt all about the process of the investigation, the dramatis personae, and, of course, the 'gruesome details'. Then I became enraptured by the fable that contaminates the history, the kind of stuff that infuriates serious students of the Jack the Ripper case: the legend of the doctor in the top hat with the Gladstone bag; wacky conspiracy theories involving Lewis Carroll, the Elephant Man, the Duke of Clarence, and the Freemasons. I was enraptured by it all, the setting most especially. London, the most mythologised of cities, had this whole other mythos weaved of its lines. I couldn't get there quickly enough, and even before I did, I felt that I understood it well. Geography—both the serious students and the conspiracy theorists agreed—was key to the Ripper case. Plotting the murder sites on a map, and the possible routes between them, brought one closer to the mind of the killer, they said: by narrowing the range of the fiend's likely home ground (the historians), or by marking the coordinates of a pentagram or some other occult symbol (the crazies). My approach was vaguer than that, if nearer in its intent to the crazies': I used to pore over the London *A to Z* street atlas in a daze, or a trance even, willing an invisible plumb line from my subconscious to stir. I would try, God love me, to psychically experience those streets, to divine from the shape of the clusters and rookeries that they formed, and even from the typographies that labelled them, what their personalities were. I noted that the names of the tiniest streets—the courts and passages—were written in a strange, tentative, almost handwritten text. One such was Mitre Square, where wretched Catherine Eddowes was torn to a shambles. It had exactly the same typeface as used in the late-Victorian *Illustrated Police News*.

I first went to London when I was seventeen, with my uncle. He's a bachelor, and still lives in the house where he grew up with his parents and my father. His mother (my grandmother) had been born in 1904 in Manchester—within sixteen years of the Ripper murders, and only a few hundred miles from where they took place. I so badly wanted to find in that house—in the attic, say, or a locked desk—a vital piece of evidence relating to the Ripper case, and strongly believed that one day I would. I remember my excitement in those dawn hours the morning of our departure to London. I thought of the streets I would finally walk, on the trail of a cast list that read like a census of *Punch* caricatures: John Pizer, Elizabeth Stride, Israel Schwartz, Frederick Abberline, PC Mizen, Polly Nichols, Martha Tabram. My itinerary would of course take in the canonical murder sites: Buck's Row (now Durward Street), Hanbury Street, Berner Street (now Henriques Street), Mitre Square, Miller's Court (now razed). And then there were the ancillary sites: the side alleys, the escape routes, the track of a bobby's beat. Goulston Street, by its very name, evoked the appeal, for many, to this case: the glamour of grisly death. Here the killer may or may not have left behind his handwriting in the graffito 'THE JUWES ARE THE MEN THAT WILL NOT BE BLAMED FOR NOTHING'. Below the daubing was found a bloodied rag, a swatch of Catherine Eddowes's apron. Most agree it was taken by Jack to clean his knife. Some suggest it was used by the penniless prostitute as a sanitary cloth.

My uncle's house was like an anteroom, an acclimatisation bell, ahead of our visit to Victorian London. It hadn't changed much in seventy years. The décor remained exactly as my grandparents had set it out, and all the ornaments they'd gathered over time—snow globes from San Giovanni, a holy water bottle from the Marian Year of 1954, a letter opener from the Eucharistic Congress year of 1932—sat on the shelves and mantelpiece where they'd first been placed. And it stank of tea: loose-leaf tea, over-stewed, furred on the crockery, soaked into the carpet. In the kitchen, a frayed rag, indelibly stained, hung undisturbed: one corner jammed in the criss-cross slit of a rubber tea-towel holder.

(When I think back to that time—the time I first became interested in Jack the Ripper—I feel a catch in my throat, and I could retch. Rumbelow tells a story of a knife, complete with blood-streaked, blue-velvet-lined leather case, gifted to a woman, in 1888, by a policeman who had kept it after a raid on the home of a Ripper suspect; the knife was then passed down a couple of generations to another woman who used it as a kitchen carving knife. I can remember how my appetite was spoiled after reading that anecdote: how chicken fat started to feel against my uvula—grainy and thick; and how chicken skin seemed chewier; and I remember the bittiness of cartilage, the sudden yield of grizzle, fragmenting between my teeth.)

Donald Rumbelow himself was the guide on our walking tour of Jack's London. I was glad of his authority, as much, as for anything else, because Spitalfields at night was a spooky place. Having travelled across London from Covent Garden to the City and then into the East End, we had left behind bright lights and clinking glasses and entered a dead zone. Deserted streets of office blocks suddenly gave way to deserted streets of tall weavers' houses and warehouses, empty and blackened like rotten teeth. The East End, as recently as the mid-nineties, still felt like the shadowy back end of the City on the Hill, an extramural slum, and it wasn't a place I would have liked to linger in on my own. There was a feeling of hostility and suspicion: not just in my imagination, I'm sure—but in the air. Locals seemed weary, at best, of the nightly parade of tourists through their quiet neighbourhood. On Hanbury Street, opposite the site of Annie Chapman's murder, an angry Bangladeshi man shouted down at us from a top-floor window of one of those whittled Huguenot homes. Rumbelow was unflappable, or perhaps just inured to abuse. He told us he had been a bobby in the last days of gaslight. I could imagine him disappearing into a peasouper with his whale-oil lamp.

We followed him to The Ten Bells, where he left us. In the 1880s the pub had been a meeting point and shelter for prostitutes. Glass cabinets now served as display cases for Ripper merchandise, and a wooden panel on the wall was even painted with the names of Jack's victims, like a roll of honour in a servicemen's club. It was all a little tacky but, nonetheless, in the dim amber light, in among the darkened wooden fittings and the misty mirrored glass, it was possible to imagine you were in the company of costermongers and seamstresses. It wasn't long before we were mellow on sweet English ale and had ceased to worry about finding a way to Aldgate East tube station and the safety of the West End.

I had a camera with me; at one stage the door to the cellar was left open, and I ventured to take a quick snap of the stairs leading down. The following week I got the reel of film developed, and—I'm not joking—there was a large smoky blob hovering in the middle of the picture.

A couple of years later I came again to The Ten Bells, with a girlfriend. In daylight, Spitalfields seemed even more depressed and shabby. It was a grey day, and the wind busted through Whitechapel High Street, west to east, rippling the surface water. We turned up Commercial Street, clinging to each other, eyes on the wet pavement, thoughts on that warming ruby ale. My girlfriend remarked that there seemed to be a lot of hookers about. It was true. Women who were patently sex workers—tottering on the tightrope of the kerb and dressed as if the sun, rather than the rain, was beating down—commanded the largely empty street. It didn't surprise me to see; I'd read that Commercial Street was still a haunt for prostitutes. Even so, I somehow didn't expect the trade to be so openly flaunted, so commonplace. In 1888, accounts speak of this street teeming with prostitutes, at all times of day, and in all weathers. We could have been seeing those very same people, trapped in a zoetrope of perpetual motion; one of the boasts of the East End was that it was the authentic London, where a way of life remained unchanged for centuries. But this—seeing these prostitutes, walking the same ground as the victims of a sexual psychopath over a hundred years earlier—felt surreal rather than real. It made me queasy about my interest in Jack the Ripper.

The lee of The Ten Bells offered some shelter from the rain, which we were thankful for, as the doors of the pub were locked. I looked about me, down the street, and then over at Christ Church Spitalfields across Fournier Street. Another Ripper landmark: this was a sort of sex-trade maypole in Victorian times, a pile around which the most desperate women of East London, dragging the ragged hems of their skirts through the rain and horse shit, performed a charade of peak-fertility for the price of a night's lodgings or cup of gin. The building was the work of Nicholas Hawksmoor, the second-most famous church-builder in London after Wren and easily the most notorious. His devotion was said to be to the occult rather than to Christianity, and a dark mythology had grown up around him and his buildings. Naturally, this mythology had become interlaced with that of the Ripper's. It was an irresistible association: writers as respected as Iain Sinclair and Peter Ackroyd had written about the pulse of Hawksmoor's satanic beacons and their significance to the Whitechapel killings. Alan Moore, in his graphic novel *From Hell*, described Christ Church as the architect's 'creed of terror and magnificence most forcefully expressed... Its tyranny of line enslaves the nearby streets, for ever in its shade.' I thought he was seeing far too much in all this. To me, Christ Church was a beautiful and well-proportioned eighteenth-century building. I was put in mind of some of Moore's other outlandish theories; for example, he dates Adolf Hitler's conception to the exact moment of one or other of the Ripper killings, as though there's only so much evil to go around, as though evil is something at all.

'Here,' said my girlfriend. She was peering through the porthole of her hands into The Ten Bells. I had a peek too; through the window I could see men, and only men, sitting on stools and chairs and all facing the same way. It wasn't obvious what they were looking at, or waiting for. Most of them were wearing builders' or tradesmen's outfits, but a good proportion, in shirts and ties, had presumably made the short journey over from Bishopsgate or other parts of the City. A member of staff—the landlord maybe—clapped his hands, and this seemed to quiet the crowd, or focus their attention: on the cellar entrance, I could see now. This same man opened the door—his face bisected by a smile and his cheeks all Toby-jug ruddy—and from below the ground a young dark-haired woman—also smiling—smoothly surfaced; head first, then bare shoulders, then barely covered chest, then barely covered loins. My girlfriend and I watched on, deeply amused. Then there was another movement—a typically burly and sallow Saxon—and we were roused to back away, and then to run.

For years and years I found myself going back and forth between Dublin and London; sometimes just to catch an Arsenal match, sometimes to crash on my brother's couch in Balham or Streatham or Tooting for extended stays. Usually, but not always, I tried to do something Ripper-related. One time I travelled out to the south bank of the Thames opposite Chiswick, where I wanted to see for myself a place called Thorneycroft's Torpedo Works. Near here, in December 1888, a month after a young Irish prostitute, Mary Kelly, was hacked to shreds in her rented room, the bloated body of one the main Ripper suspects, Montague Druitt, was found floating in the water. The coroner estimated his body had been in the river for a month; coincidentally or not, not another murder was subsequently committed, and Kelly would achieve immortality of sorts as the last canonical Ripper victim.

I don't know what I had come to see. Thorneycroft's would have been at the opposite bank of the Thames and, in any case, might not have been identifiable. In the event, I could see nothing, on that far bank, that was obviously a torpedo works. But what was I expecting? A hole in the side of a concrete bunker out of which might have slid a metal cigar? Did torpedoes even exist in 1888? Well they must have: that's how Thorneycroft's was described in 1888—a torpedo works. This was one of the bleakest places I had ever been to. The Thames was low in its trough and for yards from each bank flats of silt reached to the waterline. Distant mudlarkers—licensed scavengers—sifted the slime for coins and bones. This place, this point on the river, more or less marked the gateway to central London. On the right, all was densely grey and honey-coloured. To the left, it was mainly green. Or, at least, it might have been, would have been, only it was winter, and so it too was grey.

My interest in the story of Jack the Ripper ebbed and flowed over the years, often in accordance with how embarrassed or guilty I felt about being interested in such a macabre thing. In the last ten years it has mainly ebbed. But then the last time I studied the case it was never more intense. That was in 2010. I was meant to be pushing on with a novel that summer, but I found ample distraction in the World Cup, and then—although I can't remember what led me to discover it—I found a cache of podcasts online that analysed the Ripper case in the minutest detail. Each episode was at least an hour long, and there must have been about sixty of them. I became addicted. I wasn't happy just to snatch a few minutes of a podcast here and there; I had to listen to an episode right to the end, in one sitting, and somewhere quiet, where I could scrunch up my eyes and strain to concentrate on every esoteric piece of information. And once that was done, it wasn't enough just to listen to one episode; I had to listen through until my day was filled while more pressing and important business was pushed to the side. I became obsessed, and I became frightened in a way I hadn't felt since I was a small boy. I began to imagine that a Victorian prostitute was walking up and down the laneway behind my house. I became convinced of it. When I was a small boy I used to see the head of Saint Oliver Plunkett hover and revolve in my room, and now I felt, in a real way, the presence of this Victorian prostitute. At night I was too frightened to go downstairs to empty my bladder, and so I kept a wine bottle beside my bed that I could void myself into. One night I woke up and the woman was standing at the end of my bed. She was wearing a dark green velvet dress and her dirty blonde hair was tied up in a bun. All her features looked like they'd been chewed out of apple flesh, and a scabbed crucifix was scratched into her forehead. She clutched one hand in the other in a gesture of humility or perhaps entreaty, but then said, 'You'd say anything but your prayers. Go on, give us a shag, love.' I lobbed the wine bottle, half-filled with urine, at her, and it smashed against the wardrobe.

Night draws on the East End and it could be any age. The financial markets close, the City closes, and Whitechapel is cut adrift from the life of leisure-hour London, the other side of an empty square mile of glass. The shutters of boutique businesses come clattering down and the young clear off to the pubs and clubs of Shoreditch, Hoxton, Dalston and Clapton. There is something ominous about the air here, always, at this time. The side streets trail away in the murk. Dogs go mad in the yards of social housing. From somewhere a cry of 'Murder!' rings out. Or something like that. ('Mother!'? 'Muntered!'?) When the details of the visual world are obscured the imagination seeps to the fore; and when the imagination is geotagged to its surroundings, and aware of them in all of their dimensions—temporal as well as physical—the darkness outside and inside the head undergo a kind of osmotic transference.

Then day breaks again and new details emerge—things that look as though they have crystallised into being only that previous night. Every day now the inner East End seems radically newer than the day before. The rate of change the last decade has been as rapid as it was in the nineteenth century, the last time London was pumping with global credit. Now Spitalfields is truly integrated with the City, and not just a place for financiers to grab a cheap bagel or a lunchtime strip show, before pegging it back to their glass offices; now the offices run all the way up Commercial Street. Now the reeky defile of Hanbury Street is London's hipster high street. Now Spitalfields Market and adjacent Brushfield Street—once putrid with the run-off of market day—is as chichi a shopping destination as anywhere on the King's Road. Where at one time there were gaps in the streets, now there is the most gorgeously finished architectural infill. More and more of the Victorian grain disappears by the month; what remains is cleaned up, re-glazed, window frames toned down in fashionable greys, so as not to embarrass the swish new neighbours. This is a steampunk locale now; the past is encased, recast. From everywhere, long-legged butcher men stride in from another time: in billowy striped bloomers and felt shirts and braces, with gobbets of sauce and strings of pork in their bushy moustaches. A man in tweeds runs across the street with a growler of beer snuggled under his arm like a pig. Women's hair is tied up high, backlit by the sun. All lines lead again to London. But all lines do not lead to now; now is no longer a fixed point but a moving dial across the fixed fascia of history. The Ripper has never felt closer at hand.

Suddenly a Duck
Claire-Louise Bennett

I left home and moved to London in 1994 in order to begin a degree at a small not very reputable college in Roehampton. Despite having attained good grades in my three A-Level subjects I did not satisfy the precise requirements stipulated by Queen Mary of Westfield College, my first choice, and therefore suffered the indignity of having to 'go through clearing', which involved resentfully scouring the index of available university places published in the back pages of *The Guardian* and making last-minute calls to the various listed and lacklustre institutions with the galling optimism that some quivering milksop hadn't beat me to the post. I was incensed that Queen Mary of Westfields refused me entry, since, in terms of points, my grades were equivalent to what they'd asked for. I pointed this out to the woman on the phone in the admissions office and to the man on the phone in the English department, added to which, I said—with much emphasis and incredulity when I at last had the attention of the faculty itself—I got an A in English and you only asked for a B, and English is the very subject I wish to study! They'd wanted Bs in all three subjects and this would have worked out just fine I often suppose had I not got into an enormous pickle with my Philosophy teacher which meant that from time to time attending class was quite impossible and as such I wound up scraping a C grade. 'You ought to have done much better than that,' he said, in the pub on results day, and I felt like shoving him with all my might into the people standing in a tight-knit mirthful group directly behind him. On the other hand, one of my English teachers was absolutely flabbergasted that I'd pulled off the top mark in that subject, and openly opined that I must have cheated.

I don't quite see how it's possible to cheat at English really, but perhaps it is. Occasionally you can blag your way through areas of specific ignorance, and this I often did, but, overall, you have to have the capacity to connect with the written word, and the wherewithal to understand and relate that involvement, whatever its nature might be. In other words, if literature has the force to shape you, not your beliefs necessarily, or even your outlook, but something far more intimate and formative, the sorts of men you are drawn to, for example, and the way you experience desire, then objective analysis seems trite and becomes rather irrelevant. The value of continuing to study this most perspicacious of disciplines at such a woefully mediocre institute, where the calibre of my fellow students was generally very poor and the standard of teaching excruciatingly patchy, was negligible, and I very quickly felt frustrated and horrified that I'd ended up there. In order to give vent to these huge, barging feelings I would either archly refuse to say a word during seminars or I would set forth close readings that were complex, persuasive and entirely erroneous. I'd had some rather fanciful ideas about what studying literature at university would entail, the sorts of mellow rooms I'd pass through, the views I'd come upon, the crepuscular light, the animated hush, the slinking patina and reoccurring ferronniere, the bicycles and small bridges, everything on the turn, and, most of all, the sharp and charming people I'd meet. In fact as it turned out a great many of them liked nothing more than to sit in the middle of their beds in the middle of the day, watching Australian soap operas cross-legged with the door wide open. 'Do you want a cup of tea?' they would sometimes ask when occasionally I leant up against the door frame and scowled within. 'No,' would be the invariable reply, then I'd carry on down the corridor, possibly with the intention of having a very long hot bath in the bathroom right at the end. For the first year I lived out my unjust circumstances in the halls of residence, you see.

The first time I saw the Digby Stuart Halls of Residence was the day I arrived with my aunt and her boyfriend and moved into one of its titchy freshly-painted rooms. I'm not sure what images, prior to that, I might have seen of the building. Possibly something in a brochure—perhaps they'd sent a belated prospectus, I don't remember. There was nothing unexpected about its appearance in any case—it was several storeys high, was compiled of red brick, and had many windows going across, left to right, from where I stood anyway. I don't remember who greeted us or what the procedure was for being allocated and shown to a particular room but I recall there were two keys, one for the main door below and another for unlocking my room up on the second floor. I'm not sure what happened in the event of mislaying keys which is surprising because I'm sure I must have forgotten them fairly often. Probably it was very easy to access the dormitories, I remember going up into the dormitories in the opposite building with no great difficulty—one of the advantages of being at a small shambolic college was that although there were rules and so on they weren't assiduously enforced and so everything was near to hand without too much rigmarole, including the College Hardship Fund.

The very first thing I did was to plug in my stereo system and put on a record, one of my mother's, Marvin Gaye's 'What's Going On'. My aunt and her boyfriend hadn't hung about so I was blessedly free to get on unpacking without any upbeat interference. There was no one to tell me that one thing should go there and another thing ought to go here, and maybe where I elected to perch my kettle was precarious—I seem to remember that the shelf above it did begin to blister and peel after a while, but that might have been due to candles. Very soon after moving in it occurred to me that many things in the room would be much improved if they were completely gold so I bought a spray can of dark gold paint and set to work. I know quite a few objects received the Midas touch, but the only thing I can visually recall is a mug which now looked like a key prop from a gloomy Jacobean play about fealty and folly or whatever, added to which the tea didn't taste at all right—I didn't drink coffee then, but I'm sure if I did that also would have tasted plumbiferous and barbed. It wasn't a very big room, none of them were, and it was mostly a very untidy room, probably because I grew up in various houses that were all scrupulously clean and neat as a new pin. My mother was forever painting the banister or varnishing the front step or sanding the floorboards or scratching gloss off the windowpane with a Wilkinson Sword razor blade. One day, just before I left, a duck appeared above the toilet cistern in the bathroom at home, it was pretty quirky, compared to everything else, and came all of a sudden all at once. I wonder what else my mother might have painted—beside the duck the only other thing I remember her depicting were some flowers on a pair of stout green boots I wore to death—she used lots and lots of oil paint so the effect was very artistic and not the least bit fey.

Amazingly it was permissible to smoke in the dorms and I often smoked in bed—I think everyone probably did because no one got up terribly early, and it was quite normal to skulk off back to bed for a while in the afternoon. Overall I had some pretty disgraceful habits, for instance I'd often shimmy up onto my sink and take a pee in it during the night. Each time I did I vowed it would be the last, mostly because I saw it would be quite the catastrophe if the sink fell off the wall. How would I explain that to the nuns, I wondered, as I wiggled my bottom further into the chilly incommodious basin. There were nuns, yes. There was a pair of dead nuns buried in a vault, which I never went down to see, and two nuns upstairs, and even though they moved about a bit I never saw them either. At one time Digby Stuart College had been a College of the Sacred Heart and many vestiges of its Catholic past remained disarmingly intact. Apparently Vivien Leigh had been a pupil here, and the reason I remember that is because at around the same time, maybe a year or two before, I'd read that Vivien Leigh had been a drunk and indiscriminate nymphomaniac, too wide-ranging for Lawrence Olivier to handle, and in later years, the book tells the reader, she lifted tramps from off the street and jostled them into hedgerows in order to have sex with them. It strikes me now that this was doubtlessly a lot of exaggerated nonsense—I don't recall where exactly I read it, perhaps it was in one of those old mawkish MGM movie annuals my grandmother had so many of which aggrandise acquisitive men and demonise enterprising women. In all likelihood Vivien Leigh was very probably fairly bonkers, but why and how are not simple, sensational matters, and I was genuinely grateful for her unlikely association with this otherwise second-rate, vaguely papal, institute and its run-of-the-mill denizens.

The bathrooms were very basic and quite austere—not unlike what you might expect to find in an early-Victorian asylum or an even earlier Swiss convent. I thought it quite beautiful and it seemed natural to make prolonged visits almost every day. It was cold, sometimes very cold, the mirrors were frameless and thin, the tiles were white and the stark taps a devil to turn. The water that untwisted out of them however was clear and tapered, and soundless as fresh blown glass. There were showers of course but I almost never used them, I preferred to take a bath and I think there were two of them, though there may have been only one. Certainly there was one. In a small room with a sloping ceiling. And an off-kilter wooden chair beside it. It was a very deep, enamel bath, somewhat discoloured, and the water that billowed from the hot tap was scalding. I read somewhere that Sylvia Plath's bathwater was just about as hot as she could possibly stand it, and I was the same—I drew baths that were so hot I got giddy right away and thought I'd pass out and perhaps drown. It was painful: indeed it was a time when I was finding out about all sorts of pain, some of it methodical and self-imposed. The bathtub was where I felt private and absolutely away from everything and perhaps I pretended some things while I was there. Perhaps I pretended I was in an asylum with nothing much to do, no expectations upon me, or perhaps I imagined I was a maid in a big house doing her ablutions on a dim Sunday evening before a rapid and somewhat violent assignation with Sir halfway up the furthermost stairwell. I think the thoughts I had then probably weren't so very different from the kind of thoughts I have now: meandering, unconnected, purposeless—and slightly grubby.

There were periods, increasing in duration and tenacity, when living in halls was unbearable due to the proximity of other people. If no one saw you for a day or two, everyone would get very excited, and someone would thump on your door high up and intone your name rather heroically. I'm not sure what it was they were all worked up about—the dormitory walls were so slight you could hear your neighbour's toaster pop and I nearly always had music on, so although unseen I would have been perfectly audible. It was impossible, anyway, to be alone in a building like that, so I spent more and more time at one of the two nearby pubs: The King's Head and The Black Cat. Farther away was The Arab Boy, but I didn't frequent that particular establishment with regularity until the following year. We seldom went to The Green Man—I'm not sure why not since it was in fact very close to Putney Heath, which is where I went to live, the following year.

I saw a man on a horse, once, on Putney Heath. He was dressed in silver red livery, had a weapon on his enormous sauntering back, and the hooves of his drizzling horse left no trace in the snow. It was a foggy afternoon.

There was a pail of vomit next to the back door. I don't think it was there when I moved in, but once it was there it was difficult to remember a time when it hadn't been. It froze right through in winter and returned to its original gruelly consistency in spring. Behind the row of houses was an ancient road which most people accessed through a gate in their garden fence. The set up at our house however was somewhat less orthodox; there was a vile shed out the back that was black with fire-damage and rot, and one flailed about in a diabolical amalgam of charred remains and slippery decay before staggering out onto the ancient road. Once or twice, when I was in a particularly triumphant mood, I gave the bucket of sick a swift jolly kick before charging into the kitchen through the back door, which no one ever bothered to lock.

I threw furniture and broke things, or they smashed. Someone I became acquainted with at the time and who I still know maintains I flicked a chest of drawers across a room with just two fingers. I drank a lot of Lapsang Souchong then and would often leave mugs of it unfinished here and there so that when the surface of a piece of furniture plunged vertical several mugs went right along with it, flinging these perfectly round, velvet tapestries of mould up ahead, until they flapped and landed, like creepy little dollies, all along the bookshelves. And I drew on the walls, nothing sinister, waves mostly, with a piece of blue cue chalk I slipped off a pool table into my pocket at The King's Head one evening.

Wave after wave, each mightier than the last | Till last, a ninth one, gathering half the deep | And full of voices, slowly rose and plunged | Roaring, and all the wave was in a flame.

My friend from Nuremberg who lived a few doors down lent me a copy of *The Female Malady* and I took notes from it in the afternoon while I wrenched at pistachios and drank Ribena through a tiny straw. I collected tokens from the Ribena cartons which was very organised of me and eventually received a free Dino bubble watch for my efforts. I was very pleased with this until somehow, inexplicably, Dino turned over. His underneath was flat and pale blue and entirely featureless, and despite patiently flipping that watch over and over, ankles crossed and a cigarette sloped in my free hand, in a kind of relaxing dogged trance, Dino never came back round and was eventually buried beneath the bedside heap of sliding pistachio shale. The things I read in the book my German friend lent me shot right in beneath my skin, into that place between the nerves which is not me or even mine, that unseparate place where my grandmother and my great-grandmother are softly present, like supple shadows overlapping in an alcove. I was aware from a young age that both my grandmother and her mother had been taken into psychiatric units where they underwent brutal corrective treatment for behaviour that was considered irksome and abnormal.

In his introduction to Junichiro Tanizaki's essay 'In Praise of Shadows', Charles Moore reminds us that, 'One of the basic human requirements is the need to dwell, and one of the central human acts is the act of inhabiting, of connecting ourselves, however temporarily, with a place on the planet which belongs to us and to which we belong.' In the third year of my time in London the importance of academic achievement began to wane—discovering how to live, how to inhabit the world was a more urgent and engrossing assignment. I became very inquisitive about the contents of other people's kitchen cupboards and bathroom cabinets: an interest that endures, though less avidly, even now. But home is not simply a concrete carapace where we cook and clean and it doesn't matter how accomplished we become in those areas, they will not, on their own, engender a sense of belonging or ease.

In the third and final year I rented a large bedsit on Wandsworth Common. I had a place of my own at last, and rarely left it. I would sit for a long time, looking up at the pipes that slipped through the walls into the room, moved along the wall and disappeared out of it, onwards, to somewhere else I did not see and could not get to. These pipes, these slender interlopers, threatened and beguiled me. What a wonderful, elegant thing is a pipe, shifting in and out, up and down, throughout the building—not ending here, not beginning here, showing only a little of its passage. They seemed so important sometimes, and so graceful, the most graceful, resolute entity in here, and they were so high up and opaque that sometimes their indifference was sort of unbearable, and I wished, in a way, that I was a spider so I could see the ghostly dust on their back and perhaps make something of my own up there.

Often the home is thought of and assessed in terms of its domestic capacity, but there are other ways of interpreting and experiencing our corner of the world, and Tanizaki's beautiful book is an invitation to reimagine the purpose and feel of our intimate surroundings.

> I suppose I shall sound terribly defensive if I say that Westerners attempt to expose every speck of grime and eradicate it, while we Orientals carefully preserve and even idealise it. Yet for better or for worse we do love things that bear the marks of grime, soot, and weather, and we love the colours and the sheen that call to mind the past that made them.

Tanizaki's sensitive, idiosyncratic appraisal contrasts the Western predilection for light-filled rooms, sparkling appliances, and spotless surfaces with the Japanese tradition which favours darkness, patina, lacquer, and frailty—what Tanizaki refers to as 'the glow of grime'. Rather than fear shadows and banish them, as we do in the West, the Japanese, Tanizaki tells us, discovered how to 'guide shadows towards beauty's end'. These cultural preferences are not simply a matter of style but are indicative of attitudes to light and dark on a deeper level—it demonstrates a willingness to live cheek by jowl with phantoms, mysteries, the ancient and the chimerical. The home then is not so much a boundaried, static, place that is closed off and impervious to external influence—according to Tanizaki's wonderfully evocative descriptions, Japanese rooms are permeable and transmogrifying; infinitely capable of 'luring one into a state of reverie'.

When everything is illuminated and the shadows have been sanitised, where goes the creature inside and what happens to her daydreams? As the home becomes more domesticated, and increasingly familial, when convenience replaces ritual, and spotlights replace shades, some cosmic link is surely arrested, and the house is no longer a threshold to other worlds. The house then is nothing, just an isolated distorted edifice, tethered to its functions and possessions, and whomever lives inside there is bewildered to feel such a deep abiding estrangement in a place where she is supposed to feel protected, inspired and at ease. Perhaps she takes to her bed, perhaps she throws furniture, perhaps she draws on the walls, perhaps there is suddenly a duck, perhaps one day she simply leaves. Ungrateful creature that she is. In the exam halls, at the end of that final year, my performance was generally less than enthusiastic, and that was fine, this was a time for fantasy and nightmares, for immersion and flight—in my own rooms I had begun to understand how to live with darkness.

The blackness within you is stilled, is transfixed perhaps, when it has in its gaze the blackness without, what Tanizaki describes as a 'visible darkness'. That mesmerising preternatural and granular place, 'where always something seemed to be flickering and shimmering… This was the darkness in which ghosts and monsters were active, and indeed was not the woman who lived in it, behind layer after layer of screens and doors—was she not of a kind with them?' To be sure, merging with the dark, in all its primitive and transformative potency, is somewhat destabilising. Even so, it is surely possible, as Tanizaki says, 'to guide shadows to beauty's end', and it seems to me entirely indefensible that anyone ever thought it good and necessary to send an electric current blazing through the furrows of someone else's mind in order to dazzle the essential blackness into rapid extinction.

Letter from the Republic of London

It's been a long time since I've paid a visit, or written—
my writing was never good, and with my Liam's death
I thought things would get better
but I'm more lonely now than when we first came over
and nobody knows anyone's name round here
(if you could pronounce it)

yesterday, the neighbour from the next door flat
who never speaks, who has scars on her face
stole the yard-brush I keep outside
where I always leave it to sweep the landing—
that upset me for some reason

and the bars here are full of Irish people
I don't know, they seem cemented to the sixties
you need to have eyes like a fly round here
once, these Muslim men cursed at me for smoking
outside on the street, knocked the cigarette from my mouth
at night you treble-bar the door
and become gaga in front of the telly.

I would ask you to visit, but I don't think you'd like it
maybe when the Hammers are at home
but every work-day I disappear into the city
like all the bloodless faces going down
the steps to the subway, and I clean offices
and pretend to be deaf rather than offend

when I come back again, I listen to the neighbours fighting
in tongues. The buildings here are Shards and Gherkins
and Smoothing Irons of metal and glass
and long trains that curve through the houses
below my flat, but even twenty storeys up
the planes and the blue open sky seem such a long way off.

Gary Allen

Six Addresses

Rob Doyle

8A Stock Orchard Crescent, London N7

On my first night living in London, I slept in a garden while a light rain fell. I lay on my backpack to keep me off the cold concrete pathway. I have tried, on numerous occasions, to write about why I came to spend my first night in London sleeping rough, imagining it would make an amusing anecdote with which to open an essay such as this, or inform a lightly fictionalised scene in some future novel. But the results have always been so convoluted, the convergence of factors that led me to sleep in the garden, and not in the bed I could see through the basement window, so tediously complex, that I have given up attempting to explain it, and present you instead with the bald image: me, at twenty-six years old, lying in a garden in the rainy dark, cursing everything.

An addendum, which I also offer without explication: in the early morning, I awoke, got to my feet, and without hesitation retrieved the house-key from where it had been waiting for me all along, beneath a certain tile. I let myself in the side gate, through the back door, and into the appallingly filthy house I was to sublet from my friend S. Only a little dog named Henry was there to greet me. I soon fell in love with Henry, or at least grew as attached to him as I have ever been to any other creature, excluding four or five human beings.

On my first day in the house I walked around to Morrison's supermarket on the Holloway Road, where no one smiled and all the races converged in mutual hatred and mistrust. When I got back, I cleared off the desk in my bedroom and wrote the first lines of a novel that would take me nearly five years to finish.

A few weeks later, B, my girlfriend at the time, came to visit from the States. During her stay, she wrote a poem entitled '8A Stock Orchard Crescent'. In the poem, she and I fought acidly, and we stormed off in contrary directions along a dark road on an October evening, but there was some kind of redemption, or maybe one of us learned something, because after all it was a poem.

39 Eade Road, London N4 1DJ

When S, the friend I was subletting from, returned home, I moved into the first, cheapest place I could find. This was a mistake—you should always view at least ten houses before moving. The room I took really was desperately cheap. In London, even horrid flats cost absurd amounts of money to rent: if a place is being let for a pittance, there is a reason for it. The house I moved into was on a quiet street near Finsbury Park. I shared it with eight other people. My room was tiny—it was one of the few rooms I've ever seen that lived up (i.e. lived down) to the epithet 'box room': it really felt as if I were living in a box. Four of my housemates were Bulgarian: two couples. It wasn't me who came up with the sobriquet, 'the Vulgarians', but neither did I discourage its usage. Around dinnertime the kitchen would start getting crowded, the bottle of rakia would appear, and then the genocidal folk songs would begin in earnest. These were translated for me, grinningly and with slaps on the back, by an interpreter confident that I would approve of the sentiments expressed. I remember one song in particular: a boisterous chant about a tank commander who drove his vehicle headlong into a camp full of gypsies.

Things did not end well between the Bulgarians and me: there were death-threats and stand-offs; a bread-knife was brandished. I came to loathe them, and they me, with an intensity I have rarely experienced. Ivajlo, one of the Bulgarians, had no job but was an ardent consumer of hard-house music and weed. He was a DJ, except all his DJing was done in his bedroom, and the only people who could hear what he played—who could not *but* hear what he played—were his housemates, one of whom—me—was trying to write a novel. Ours was a cramped and thin-walled house, and the music that Ivajlo blasted every day from morning until evening did not make for an attractive living situation, nor even a liveable one. I was working at a language school in Bayswater, beside Hyde Park, on the other side of the city. In order not to let the teaching work interfere unduly with the writing of my novel, I taught only one class per day. It took me almost as long, and twice as much energy, to cycle to and from the school as it did to teach the class. When I got home around noon, I would eat something, then doze on the couch for a few minutes (my exhaustion won out over the pounding beats). Refreshed, I would fix a flask of coffee and cycle to Stamford Hill Library, where I would spend the rest of the day writing.

B came to stay in the summer. Almost a year had passed since we'd been together last. I decided that this was no house to host a lady.

Flat 97, Woolridge Way Tower Blocks, Loddiges Road, London E8

My friend Roy and his French girlfriend Nancy were leaving town for a while, so they let B and me mind their flat. It was a council flat in a high-rise block off Mare Street, up on the fourth floor. Roy and Nancy were subletting from a man who I only ever heard referred to as Peter Pan. He was long-term unemployed, terminally ill, possibly had some mental or physical disability, and had lately gone to live in Thailand for a year, minimum. Strictly speaking, it was illegal for Peter Pan to sublet his council flat, but it's a common practice, and there was no other way he could have got to Thailand without losing it. I never met Peter Pan, but I did see a photo of him on an ID card Roy showed me. He was in his late fifties, with long, stringy hair. Periodically he sent Roy emails from Bangkok updating him on the drugs he was taking—copious— and the girls he was having sex with, most of whom seemed to be prostitutes. He had gone to Thailand in the awareness of his impending death, with the frank intention of enjoying a prolonged orgy of sex and drugs; this seemed then and still seems to me a reasonable course of action. I don't know whether Peter Pan is still alive, or if he ever came back from Thailand.

B and I stayed at the flat for a few weeks. The rear balcony looked onto a courtyard that was closed in on four sides by tower blocks. Children played in the courtyard throughout the day. Perched halfway up the side of each block was a motion-sensing camera that whirred about from morning till night, always trained on the courtyard but changing direction ceaselessly, as if suffering from ADHD or undergoing psychic implosion. By this time, I had got through a couple of drafts of my novel and was teaching at a school in Islington, a more reasonable distance from home. Rejection letters were coming in at a steady pace. B flew to Boston to begin an MFA in poetry—we planned to reunite in the winter—and I moved into a house in Hackney.

58 Narford Road, London E5 8RD

I've just used Google Maps to street-view the house where I lived for a couple of years, just down from Stoke Newington High Street and the sleazy basement nightclubs of Dalston. The street-view photos were taken in 2012, while I was living there: the window of the front room is still boarded up—we never got around to sorting that out—and a clutter of bins and buckets fill the strip of cement we had for a front garden. My housemates were Damon, a Londoner in his mid-thirties who managed the parks in the area, and Garry, a permanently stoned Mancunian and recovering alcoholic in his forties, who rarely left his basement room when he wasn't working (his job was to sit outside shopping centres and persuade people to set up standing orders for the World Wildlife Federation). When Garry moved out, he was replaced by Laure, a young gay woman from Luxembourg, who was even more reclusive—and, to me, more intriguing—than her predecessor. I became friends with Damon: we bonded over a shared fondness for recreational drug abuse. When B came to stay for a few weeks after finishing her Masters, however, I was judged to be acting unfairly by bringing an extra person under the roof. The situation soured— Damon and Laure turned against me. Then summer came and we made up, sitting out in the vine-strewn back garden with our shirts off, drinking cans. I went out one night to a Dalston club with Laure; I was high and it felt a little awkward because I think she thought I fancied her, which I did, in spite of the obvious. Then I flew to San Francisco, chasing after B, hoping to make it work, or if nothing else, to see what it was like to live in California for a while.

109 South End Close, London NW3 2RE

The following winter, B and I moved back to London, into a fifth floor flat in Hampstead, by the Heath. Once again we were subletting less than legally— this time from an American in his sixties named Erwin who had written a book on Jack the Ripper, and his partner Raquel, a graphic novelist. The couple were also booksellers, with a stall on Hampstead High Street, and the cosy, cave-like flat was crammed with books. Not only was each room the repository for hundreds of books (some rooms had *nothing* but books in them), but the narrow hallway was lined on both sides with stacks of books that reached to the ceiling. The flat afforded views of the London skyline. Helpfully, a pair of binoculars had been left in two of the rooms. I got into the habit of lurking by the window in the evenings with the lights off, Tindersticks or Duke Ellington playing on the stereo, and peering at the activities taking place behind the windows of other blocks, or at the lit-up skyscrapers of the City or Canary Wharf, thinking like a terrorist.

Three and a half years had passed since I had written the first lines of my novel. I had amassed many, sometimes reluctant rejection letters, and been invited for meetings with publishers who changed their minds at the last moment ('Too bleak, too misanthropic, too negative,' they said. 'You don't know the half of it,' I thought). My short fiction had begun to get published, however, and I was starting to achieve, if not a name for myself, at least a modicum more visibility than I'd possessed during the preceding years of total obscurity.

B's parents had been against her moving back to the UK with me, and against our planned marriage, and against my very existence, or so I came to think (the same might be said of any number of the fleeting figures who populate this story). We never did get married: at the end of her six-month visa, with Erwin and Raquel about to move back into the Hampstead flat, B returned to the US. There have been a few emails, but I haven't spoken to her since.

20b Finsbury Park Road, London N4 2JZ

For my last ten days living in London, I stayed at the current flat of S, the friend in whose garden I had slept on my first night in the city, four years previously. For reasons that are too complex to go into here, S and I are no longer speaking. Nor does he still live in London. Most of the friends I knew in those years have moved on—to Hong Kong, Central America, Australia, the US, Ireland, France. On my last night at S's place, we stayed up very late, drinking whiskey and listening to the album we had crafted together over the past three years, recently finished. I slept for an hour or two, woke hungover, and was lucky not to miss the train that took me away from the city, across the English and Welsh countryside, to the ferry-port at Holyhead. There, I boarded the Ulysses and sailed to Dublin. While crossing the Irish Sea, I finished a short story I'd begun the day after B left London, about a writer who returns to Dublin—on the Ulysses—after a long time away, wondering if he's just exchanging one loneliness for another.

It is difficult, when we look back on certain periods of our lives—the years we spent living in London, for instance, in our twenties, writing a book and loving as much as we knew how to—not to fall into the trap of romanticism and nostalgia. Even while I lived in London, though, I romanticised the city and the life I lived there; or rather, I knew it *was* a beautiful, romantic time of life, and that, like youth itself, the circumstances that had come so magically together would never be repeated, and that one day I would miss those years, the limitlessness of it all. I also knew, or suspected, that romanticism serves another purpose: it puts a veneer on the squalor and disorder of our days, relieving us of having to look too squarely at the sadness underlying them, and the pain we cause ourselves and others—though such knowledge does creep in, inevitably, at the frayed end of some weekend-long session, in the eerie chemical silence. I haven't been back to London since I lived there, but I don't need Heraclitus to remind me that you can't step into the same city twice. The London where I lived no longer exists, any more than a dream exists upon awakening—a dream in which you were happy, in which life lived up to its promise.

Some notions of home

Niamh Mulvey

There's not much I like about Ireland. I prefer London's cosmopolitanism, America's fiction, Scandinavia's politics, France's sex scandals, Spain's food, the way Japanese girls wear flat shoes, Berlin's exuberance. I'm also a fan of Paris after the war, New York in the fifties, St Petersburg in the springtime, and I like subways, huge suburbs and getting lost and not knowing anyone, anyone at all, as far as the eye can see…

There's not much I like about Ireland, so I live in London. When I moved here a few years ago, my boyfriend and I lived in a shared house with several others, people we didn't know. A Polish builder, in his sixties at least, rented the sitting room. It was one of those deceptively enormous Victorian terraced houses built as part of the south London railway suburbs in the late nineteenth century. According to Charles Booth (this guy who walked the thousands of streets of the city in the 1890s classifying neighbourhoods and describing his findings in meticulously swoopy handwriting), back then the house would have been home to an upper middle-class family who would have been likely to 'keep a servant, or at least a girl'. (Perhaps Irish, right? From Cork, like how your basic Irish servant girl is always from Cork.) Anyway, we had the front room of this lovely, but draughty old house, while the Polish guy lived in the next room, what used to be the living room. He was handsome—incredible cheekbones—and he used to try to get my fella to watch YouTube videos of Christian proselytising in the sticky little kitchen we all shared. He paid little attention to me, and would direct all questions to the male of our relationship, which I didn't really mind. I think he meant to be gentlemanly. When he walked down the hall you could smell the dusky smoke of his weird cigarettes in the air for quite a while afterwards. It wasn't an entirely unpleasant smell, but he wasn't supposed to smoke in the house.

Upstairs lived an unfriendly BBC worker who informed us, coldly, when we asked—we always had to ask, back then, we had to know—that she was Iranian-Finnish. Later, a curiously dead-eyed young man from the north of England moved into another room. He worked in an art gallery and was always in his room, throttling the internet connection with his dubious bit-torrents. A woman of Caribbean extraction owned the house. She was funny and generous and allowed us to pay the deposit on the room over two months because, she said, this must be an expensive time for you. Her surname was Walsh, so I asked her about it (of course). She shrugged and said something about a priest in Jamaica several generations ago who christened a load of people with Irish surnames. Why are you moving to cold grey London, she asked, laughing a bit at me. I viewed the house one freezing day in February having spent weeks crashing on an friend's couch and house-hunting in the dark evenings after work, stupidly scheduling viewings in Shepherd's Bush and Hackney half an hour apart. I'm from Ireland, I said. And then she laughed a bit more. I took the room with huge relief.

When you wake up to news stories about Sudanese people trying to scramble across the English channel straight into Farage heartland, you think of all the times you've thought about your Irishness and you blush very deeply indeed. I am an emigrant, I suppose, but often that feels far too grandiose a term for a white girl who works in a shiny office in central London and can afford to come home a couple of times a year.

So, I am very much into checking my privilege, because this is about the extent of it: every year your 'r's get a little flatter and your 'th's softer and you find yourself saying entire sentences in some strange bastardised London commuter accent: *Can you move dahn, please.* On the way out of Dublin airport on your way back home, you see those signs about cash prizes for bringing companies into the country, lovely Saoirse Ronan's lovely face reminding you to do your bit—and you do feel annoyed, for a moment, by the desperation of it, the 'we really don't have a clue how to keep you here, but got any change on ya' of it all. But you forget about it pretty quickly. And then when *The Guardian* is running opinion pieces on the latest Ireland cock-up, people don't usually ask you about it, because they're not interested, but you want to tell them about it anyway. You want them to know—yes, they forced that girl to have a Caesarean; no I can't vote, unless I go home, and even then I'm not really supposed to—and you want them to be a bit shocked. Why? Because, as Tommy Tiernan once said: *What does being Irish mean? It means you're not fucking English*. This is England, after all. The whole thing, it's still there, sort of, in the way you bristle when someone makes a joke about the 'potato' famine and the way you respond to your colleague when he asks you about getting his (British) passport renewed: *I don't fucking know, mate.*

But it's not that you're ungrateful, oh no. It's London that trusted you enough to give you a job in the industry you wanted to work in. It's London that gave your partner a job within days of arriving, following months on the dole and a joke of an internship on a JobBridge scheme. But it's not that you blame Ireland, either, oh no. It's your own fault for wanting to do something different. It's your own fault for not wanting to stay working in a take-away in the evenings while you interned during the day. It's your own fault for not filling in those HDip application forms. So that's where you end up—grateful to London, and not angry at Ireland, no, not one bit.

And really, in this day and age, what does it matter? Britain isn't even owned by its citizens anymore—the whole country is being sold off to the highest bidder, and central London is populated almost exclusively by foreign millionaires though these people never feature in the endless debates they have here about immigration. If you bring enough capital to a country, it seems you can enter yourself, soundlessly and without fanfare, though arguably this wealth distorts British society in a far more radical way than any amount of ordinary people from Eastern Europe. We're never mentioned either, English-speaking, white as we are, UKIP considers us 'kith and kin', and, if you're not careful, you end up in the curious position of demanding acknowledgment of your 'otherness' while those with real challenges do all they can to overcome it.

So it's not a lot to worry about, is it? Do Pennsylvanians living in Florida write anguished pieces about their feelings of dislocation? Maybe they do (I'd definitely read them), but likely they don't, much. So us 'new' Irish in London, with our education and our sexiness, and our wheely suitcases perfect for Ryanair weekends at home, we're nothing like the depressing number of older men you encounter, like the one I saw last weekend, arguing in pure Dublinese while topping up his electricity card in the corner shop, drunk as a skunk at midday, or the man who asked me for change in Soho last summer and who, it turned out, was raised in an orphanage not half a mile from where I grew up. We're nothing like that. Us new snazzy Irish 2.0, we're grand sure. And because of this—our diluted, lily-livered emigrant experience—there's not a huge amount we can complain about. We ask each other, do you ever think of going home? And, mostly, we answer each other vaguely: we don't know, maybe, depends, and then we change the subject because maybe it's too much effort. Maybe we'll just stay forever, because why wouldn't we. Sure it's no distance.

And sometimes, I think about going home and being older, and my own kids coming back over here, or going away somewhere even further and staying there, and what's the point? Why would I give up all of the things that are so much better for me here, just to go back to some notion of home, only for it all to work out in the exact same way again? And then you're slap back up against the politics of it all—what's going to become of our little country? And of course you're excluded from all of that anyway. (Even your friends back home tell you, nervously, that they don't think emigrants should have the vote. Maybe in the fun stuff like the referendums. But not for the Dáil. That would only distort things.)

You don't want anyone to feel sorry for you. You don't say 'press' for cupboard anymore, boo fucking hoo. Us Irish, we love our drama and our tragedy, and sometimes, there just isn't any. Sometimes, there is just living somewhere that looks exactly like home, but feels completely different. Sometimes homesickness goes away, and then you're left with just another choice.

So what does it matter? There's not much I like about Ireland anyway. Except my family and friends, of course. There's not much I like about Ireland. Except, you know, thinking about it quite a lot. There's not much I like about Ireland. Except being there.

A Woman in Transit

Edna O'Brien

This is not a meditation on either nostalgia or alienation. I left Ireland willingly, but I doubt that I would have found the freedom to write if I had stayed there, as the obstacles and scrutiny were oppressive. I wanted to write and in my marginalised situation as a chemist's apprentice in Cabra, I learnt of a literary coterie who nightly convened in the Pearl Bar, the talk and banter grandiloquent, and including at least two geniuses, Flann O'Brien and Patrick Kavanagh. However, in a cartoon of that time, these literati are depicted standing shoulder to shoulder, an all-male phalanx guarding their secrets of the Holy Grail. The giants that hovered over every would-be poet and penman, were of course Joyce, who was dead, and Beckett the Blasphemer, as good as dead, having fled to Paris. He was called the Blasphemer in an Irish paper, because he had defamed the name of Jesus Christ. The myths were receding. Yeats had foretold that a crowd would gather and not know there was that thing 'that seemed a burning cloud'. He was referring to Maud Gonne McBride. In fact, and I took it to be most auspicious, I saw Maud Gonne myself one day, outside the Unicorn Restaurant, all in black with a black veil, so tall she had to stoop to hear her listeners, her bearing like that of an ancient queen.

As for alienation, I did not, as so many exiles have had to do, start again with a nascent language, even if it was soon clear to me that the Irish and the English grapple with it in a different way.

I arrived, with my small sons Carlo and Sasha, at Waterloo Station on November 9th 1958. The boys were in their element, having no school for at least a week and in the buffet on the train journey, down from Liverpool, the waiter presented them with several little pots of jam and marmalade. The glass dome that covered the vast purlieu of Waterloo Station was sooted, and the pigeons beyond also seemed black and divested of nature. Though choosing to live in a city, I missed nature and I still do. In my room in London, where I work, when I sometimes hear the clip-clop of horse hooves going by, I am immediately transported to County Clare and a picture of horses in a sudden and unaccountable maraud, galloping as if to some great challenge.

Our new home was in outer suburbia, genteel though not affluent and there were no Irish people that I knew of. Camden Town and Cricklewood was where they converged, most of the men working on building sites and the young women either training to be nurses or chambermaids. The Bohemian London that I aspired to seemed to centre around two bars, one in Soho and one next to the BBC in Langham Place, where Louis MacNiece, Dylan Thomas and Seamus Ennis were often engaged in heated rapport. In those early days, feeling stranded as I was, I had this notion that one day I would be initiated into the literary echelons of London, the hidden Ithaca. Meanwhile, I brought my sons to the local school and began to write *The Country Girls*, which seemed to be waiting in the wings, a tale of longing and defiance and for which I had received and already spent the sum of fifty pounds.

I had already decided that the English were somewhat cold-hearted and with a dismaying ignorance of Irish humour and I was both seeking and avoiding reminders of home. I went to Mass of course and fled on the way out, in case the priest would collar me. I sought out markets and stalls that were reminiscent of Moore Street in Dublin, where high-spirited women sold tablecloths, lace runners and sprigs of white heather for luck. My favourite market and by far the most exotic was on Portobello Road, a whole street of treasures and people much friendlier and lackadaisical. Around St Patrick's Day, I thought it was tantamount to a miracle if I happened to be sent shamrock from home, with the clay still stuck to it. It brought to my mind the spell that had been put on Saint Columba, who, when banished from Ireland and told he could never set foot on it again, had the soil of Iona adhered to his boots. I did not much care for the more raucous St Patrick's Day shenanigans, too much sentimentality, too brash.

I'd had one epiphany, as they are called, by reading a chapter from *Portrait of the Artist* in a bookshop in Bachelor's Walk in Dublin—I was gripped by not only the genius of it, but by its truth and simplicity. The second epiphany happened when I attended a lecture on Ernest Hemingway at London University, given by Arthur Mizener. He read the first pages from *A Farewell to Arms* and those spare words, with so much narrative and feeling within them, were a further whet to the work

I had begun. With publication, there was some small acclaim in England, anger and repugnance at home. The literary hoopla I had envisaged did not occur. What I did not know was that a brisk correspondence had started up between the then Catholic Archbishop of Westminster and Charles Haughey, both attesting to the depravity of the book and the fact that it should not be allowed in any decent home. As with Synge (one of my abiding heroes), I was accused of having brought 'a smear on Irish womanhood'. To this day, London taxi drivers, who marvel that I have not lost my Irish accent, assure me that their mothers, or maybe by now it is their grandmothers, have read the 'dirty book'. If as many people had read that book as claim to have done, then I would be a rich woman indeed.

So it was on to the next book, *Girl with Green Eyes*, while secretly rebelling against the constraints of my marriage and lonely suburbia. Two years later and in gothic fashion, I left my husband and after some vicarious times in various lodgings, wrote the third book of the trilogy, *Girls in their Married Bliss*. I would meet my children at railway stations or at the school gates and so began a long and ugly battle for custody, in which local doctor, school headmaster and other notables attested to my unsuitability as a mother. So Ireland wasn't the only place with a big stick.

In that grim time I had one encounter with an Irish man, which has stayed with me, because his loneliness mirrored mine. I was on the top of a double-decker bus, coming back from White City (where I had gone to do a BBC interview), when a man came and sat next to me. Without ado he said, in a voice that was surely Tipperary, 'Wouldn't it be great now to be out the fields at home hunting ferrets?' I could not invite him in for a cup of tea at the lodgings, as visitors were not allowed, but we sat on a park bench and, as they say, ruminated.

With the money from *Girls in their Married Bliss* I bought a little house, number 9 Deodar Road, and started giving parties, which got more lavish with time. These generated great interest, were sometimes written about in gossip columns, envied and of course derided. It was imagined that I was now part of a swinging sixties group, with ne'er a care on me. Nothing could be further from the truth. It is in no way a reflection on the English, but at my parties the guests were always from elsewhere— Canadian, American, European, Scottish. The guest of honour was always and would always be Sean Kenny, the theatre designer, who carried in his bones the genius and essence of Ireland.

I did not feel confident enough to write about London until many years later. First was a play, *Haunted*, concerning a married couple, also relegated to the margins and, like Thoreau's characters, leading lives of quiet desperation. It was triggered, the way all my works are triggered, by accident. In a newsagent's in Morden, near where we lived, there was a handwritten sign which said: *Widower wishes to dispose of recently deceased wife's clothing, as good as new. Call evenings.* My second prompting came from Sasha, who described to me an older man, one of Beckett's dreaming Belacquas, who was having a quiet drink in a pub on St Patrick's Day, when the motley, in their variety of greens, arrived for the festivities, whereupon he left. It led me to north London, to centres where some of the Irish labourers, now retired, came to play billiards, to chat and to have a bit of free lunch. I often met them there and invariably we repaired to pubs, where I met many others who had once upon a time come to seek work, with a crucifix and pyjamas in the suitcase and steadfast memories of mother. Their stories were rich and they told them unstintingly and with a blazing and inspired truth, eons away from the Paddy jargon.

I have lived happily in London, or as happy as my anxious temperament allows, for the last fifty-seven years and the only brouhaha that happened was when I wrote a profile of Gerry Adams for *The New York Times*. There followed my novel, *House of Splendid Isolation*, but it was the newspaper article that people mostly read and were incensed by. Some spoke to me with absolute disbelief that I would show sympathy towards such people and such a cause, while others were openly intemperate and an MP at a gathering told me that he would bring back hanging for the likes of me. It was useless to cite history, useless to talk of Shankill Butchers or B-Specials, or the long years of Catholics in the North being treated as second-class citizens. But I believed then as I believe now that the partition of Ireland was ill-judged, brutal and had drastic consequences.

Having said at the outset that I imagined being initiated into a magic literary circle, I know now that there is no such thing, because writing is a lonely business and the only lasting magic is through language.

I am here, I have written without interruption or fisticuffs, I have met with warmth from many people in many walks of life and am happy to report on some faithful readers. Yet I am a woman in transit and when my time comes, I will lie with my ancestors on a grave on Holy Island on the Shannon. 'A quiet watered land', as one of the poets wrote of a sister island, birds and water birds whirling in and out over the roofless chapels and oratories, and maybe those roses that haunt me, part flower, part bloodshed, nature and sacrifice as one.

High Street Kensington

I exit the rush-hour underground and it's you
I find, hurrying along the night-time street.
You came over in '56, you and my father seeking
work, too poor to marry in Fermoy. You found
your first London job in the basement of Barkers.

I scrutinise the old chocolate-brown building,
no longer a genteel department store, the lower floor
a giant Whole Foods mall. But you're here, you're
here in the geometric Art-Deco façade—was it built
in 1930, the year of your birth? They've put you

in Haberdashery, buffing the walnut counter till your face
is ablaze in amber. But when you get the chance
you pull open a shallow drawer, lift a spool of ribbon—
'eau de nil'—feel the watered silk between your fingers
as you measure it against the brass yard-stick.

I cross the road to St Mary Abbots, its gothic shadows
skipping round floodlit gargoyles and buttresses.
What do you make of the steel-grey steeple? Shoppers
swirl round the fulcrum of its pencil-thin elegance,
oblivious to the ease with which it spikes the Kensington sky.

You cross the road in your lunch-hour to peruse
the flamboyant carvings. Taught to fear Protestants,
you don't dare to go in, though you'd give a week's wages
to sit at the midday recitals by students from the Royal
College of Music, stand outside instead, listening—

Exsultate, jubilate, o vos animae beatae, dulcia cantica canendo.
The priory is still overlooked by the latticed towers
of Barkers, lit up so I can see two Union Jacks flapping,
but where are the red-domed buses—double-deckers—
open at the back, with landing platform and steel pole

for gripping when you jump on? Which one do you take
from your lodgings in Fulham, to get you here for 9 AM?
Making my way back to the station, the heels of your
new court shoes ring out on the pavement. You're here,
twenty-five, hurrying to the tube that will whisk you

to the Opera, to your narrow seat in the gods.

Mary Noonan

On the South Bank

On a crisp winter's day half a world away
from the ones I loved, I sat on a bench dedicated
to people who shared this view, once. Who
watched the Thames throwing itself against
the concrete walls, who may too have closed
their eyes, imagined the shouts of children
running through the giant bubble blown
by a man in a T-shirt in December,
were their nephews and nieces.

I thought I saw, amongst the crowds fleeing
the National with scarves and programmes
fluttering, my long-necked mother striding out,
my broad-shouldered father encasing her
in his coat. Fighting the wind which threatened
snow, seeking out a corner snug or bulbous black
cab to spirit them away to a place where the record
player scratched out the Tarantella's rhythm.

What would they make of this place?
The ebb and flow of tourists and commuters—
trainer clad and coffee clutching,
cameras dangling like gothic necklaces?
Hungry for a taste of home, I walked on,
though evening was rushing after me. I
found myself again, on a bench, staring at
the *Portrait of a Young Woman*, more at home
above our kitchen table than in the Tate's
echoing hall.

Catherine Higgins-Moore

How to Be Irish from a Distance

With the palm of your right hand, slap the back of your left.
This is a slight, so face north-west and aim it at Ireland.
And be patient: speechlessness takes time to ferment.
Practise this until it stings, make sure it's understood.
Listen now for the president's gasp when it arrives, sun-smacked
And citric-bitter, and sounding for all the world like disapproval.
Now swim. Redden lightly on both sides. Learn the words for colour.
Repeat: Golden Virginia *prasino*; Rizla *prasino*; *filtrakia prasino*.
Remember ws are os, vs are ns, and arguments merely discussions.
Read in the original. Feign enlightenment.
Write your own myths about size and stamina
By taking one to bed, and apply your findings to all of them.
Pack light, text home, make lists. Don't always trust the water.
If nothing else, realise this: you cannot be absented
From yourself. Go, by all means, but take a mirror. Stand before it.
With the palm of your right hand, slap the back of your left.

David Nash

Silhouette
Danielle McLaughlin

Her mother's room was on the second floor with a view of the river and the Coca Cola bottling factory on the opposite bank, neat rows of red and white trucks resembling from this distance a child's toy collection. Aileen had planned to deliver her news on Friday evening; that way, if things didn't go well, her mother would have time to come round before Aileen had to leave again on Sunday. But fog at Heathrow delayed her flight and then there was a queue at the car-hire desk in Cork and a problem with a form, so it was almost 8PM before she arrived at the nursing home.

'Aileen,' her mother said, 'you're late.' Her mother was propped up in bed, her slight frame barely denting the pillows. Settled by her bedside, in the room's only chair, was Eily, one of the other residents. Eily was tall as well as broad, her white curls adding several inches to her height, and when she leaned forward in the chair, she eclipsed Aileen's mother almost entirely.

'Sorry,' Aileen said, 'my flight was delayed,' but her mother and Eily had already resumed their conversation. It was something about the new podiatrist, and his tendency to be rough with the pumice stone. Her mother's problems, being terminal, were far beyond the reach of podiatry, but still, she debated the subject of calluses with an intensity that was unsettling. Aileen went to stand by the window while she waited for them to finish. Their conversation had a curious dynamic—a decorous yet vaguely malicious chipping away at each other, the way a child might pick slyly at a scab. It occurred to her, fleetingly, that were she to deliver her news now, Eily's presence might possibly temper her mother's response. It wasn't that her mother had anything against grandchildren; but Aileen's sister Janet had already provided four and the circumstances of Aileen's pregnancy—43, unplanned, married work colleague—were not what her mother would have hoped for.

The nursing home had once been a convent and it retained a cloistered feel. Cell-like rooms branched like pods off narrow stalks of corridors and in the wall behind her mother's bed, there was a curious rectangular indent where it looked like a door had been papered over. Usually when she was home from London, she stayed in her mother's house in Ballyphehane, empty these days apart from a cat the neighbours had been entrusted with feeding. But Janet, her sister, had rung earlier in the week to say that this time Aileen should book a hotel. There was now a tenant in their mother's house, because, as Janet had rather bluntly put it, it wasn't as if their mother would be moving back in. Aileen imagined a stranger, a girl—because for some reason she was sure the new tenant was a girl—working her way through the house, opening first one drawer, then another. 'I guess this is what it feels like to be burgled,' she'd said to Janet.

Janet had sighed. 'It's nothing like being burgled,' she said. 'Why does everything have to be such a drama with you? I was only saying that to Mam the other night.'

'So Mam knows?'

'About the house? Gracious, no! We were talking about something else.'

'But what about my things?' Aileen had said. She'd pictured the girl—in clearer relief now: fair-haired and fine-boned and dressed like a cat burglar—finding diaries from Aileen's teenage years, items of greying underwear forgotten in the hot press.

'You haven't lived in that house in twenty years,' Janet said. 'What things could you possibly have there? If it makes you feel any better, I moved a lava lamp and a box of ornaments up to the attic.'

It was late May and the evening was still bright. Outside in the grounds, neatly pruned shrubberies descended into briars and mounds of fermented grass cuttings as they approached the river. Since Aileen's visit the previous month, floods had taken away part of the boundary fence, and someone had bridged the gap with a length of blue rope, tied between posts like a finish line. It was tempting fate, Aileen thought; it was downright irresponsible in a place like this. She imagined her mother and Eily, shuffling and elbowing, as they tumbled downhill to land head over calloused heels in the black mud of the riverbed.

Eventually, Eily stood up, gathering her dressing-gown around her, and shuffled towards the door. She paused to raise a hand, hip height, in half-salute, though her expression was so vexed the gesture could just as easily have been interpreted as a threat. When Aileen sat in the vacated chair, it still held traces of Eily's warmth, and she took off her coat and folded it underneath her to serve as a cushion.

'I knew all the Dennehys from Liscarroll,' her mother said, 'and there was never any of them a dentist.' A filigree of bruises from the hospital drip was visible on the inside of one arm. 'There was a Dennehy a vet all right,' she said, 'a vet of sorts, but never a dentist.' This was her mother's latest pastime: scrutinising Eily's ancestry. Each new fragment was committed to memory to be dissected in Eily's absence, inconsistencies hunted down with a doggedness usually reserved for war criminals. Her mother's hand crept across the blankets and beat up and down at the edge of the bed. 'Janet brought me a book the other night...' she said, 'You might as well take it away.' The book, a copy of *The Road*—a curious choice for the terminally ill, Aileen thought—had fallen to the floor and Aileen picked it up, put it back on the locker. 'Take it with you when you're going,' her mother repeated, 'Things only go missing here,' and she rolled her eyes in the direction of Eily's room.

From the corridor came the squeak of rubber-soled shoes, and a trundling of wheels. A young woman in a blue aide's uniform parked a trolley in the doorway. 'How are we this evening?' she said, squeaking her way across the floor. She lifted Aileen's mother's hand and placed a finger on the underside of her wrist. The finger was plump and fat. Aileen's mother's skin was almost transparent, veins winding in blue rivers beneath the surface.

'Dorene,' her mother said, 'this is my other daughter, Aileen.'

Dorene let go of her mother's hand and took a pen from the pocket of her uniform. She wrote something on the chart clipped to the bottom of the bed. 'Daughter?' she said, as she peeled back the blanket and sheets on one side, 'why, you could be sisters.'

Aileen felt offended, then immediately guilty, for was her mother not entitled to this at least, this small, transparent lie? She watched Dorene place a hand on her mother's back and roll her onto her side, as her other hand pulled taut the undersheet. There was something supremely confident in the way Dorene, who couldn't be more than thirty, moved her mother: easily, matter-of-factly, a careless squandering of touch as if this was something she did every day, which of course it was. Aileen suddenly felt very tired; tired and incompetent. If she could lift the baby out now she would. She would pass it, red and dripping, across the bed to Dorene. Dorene would know what to do with it. And Aileen knew then that she wouldn't be able to tell her mother about the baby this evening; she wouldn't be able to tell her anytime in this strange place that was half-motel, half-mortuary.

'I thought we might go for a drive tomorrow,' she said, as soon as Dorene had gone. 'Just you and me. I thought we might go to the seaside.'

*

'I could ask Janet to drive us,' her mother said next morning, as they stood in the porch of the nursing home. As she spoke, she patted the outcrop of silver curls at the nape of her neck, a nervous habit she'd had since Aileen was a child, though the curls had been brown then, and thicker.

'I know how to drive, Mam.'

'It would be no trouble to Janet,' her mother said, staring at the car parked beside the kerb. 'She could be here in twenty minutes.' Aileen knew then that her mother had already asked Janet; that Aileen's driving—the likely hazards of it—had been debated in apocalyptic fashion until all her mother's troubles, even her illness, had paled beside the threat of a daughter home from London in a rented Fiat. Reminding herself that she mustn't fight with her mother, Aileen said nothing, just linked her mother's arm and walked her to the car.

They drove south along the coast with the sea on one side and on the other, ditches swollen with gorse and the lush, wanton grass of early summer. Last night, in a three star hotel on the edge of the city, Aileen had taken out a map and decided they would go to Courtmacsherry where her mother's family came from and where her mother had holidayed each summer when she was a child. Her mother was a poor passenger, flattening herself back against the seat every time they rounded a corner. Her hand flew to her throat if they overtook a lorry. Not a driver herself, she wasn't prepared to believe Aileen was one either.

Janet texted to say she would meet them for coffee in Kinsale. Couldn't she have allowed her this one day alone with their mother? Aileen thought. But there was no safe way of saying this to Janet, no way that mightn't end in a row, so she'd said yes, of course, yes, please join us. Aileen and her mother were first to the café and sat at a table by the window. Aileen ordered coffee and a scone. Her mother ordered a pot of tea and a boiled egg, though boiled eggs weren't on the menu, then went to use the bathroom. Aileen thumbed through a copy of a local newspaper. She'd noticed a shift these past few weeks, her gaze falling on things previously skipped over, and now it settled on an article about hatches in Germany where women could leave their babies. She imagined something like the clothes recycling unit outside her office. Babies tipping over into warm, scented heaps of other babies, downy and milky and sleeping; babies plopping into warm darkness, the occasional soft cracking of skulls like eggs.

From behind the bathroom door she heard the muffled drone of the hand-dryer, a drowsy, muted buzzing, like a bee trapped in a curtain fold. It stopped, started up again, stopped again. Her mother came out, wiping her hands on a paper tissue. 'I don't know why they bother with those things,' she said. She sounded more relaxed now, heartened perhaps by the fact that they had arrived unscathed. She took a plastic tub from her handbag and shook a blue, cylindrical pill into her palm. Placing it on her tongue, she took a mouthful of tea and tipped back her head in a quick, jerky movement. She pressed a napkin to her lips, held it there a moment.

Janet's car pulled up outside. The eldest child, Keith, the one who looked most like Janet's husband Richard, was in the passenger seat, the other three strapped into booster seats in the back. Janet took a while to parallel park, the people-carrier awkward and cumbersome, grazing the bumpers of the cars in front and behind. Then she swivelled round in the driver's seat, presumably, Aileen thought, to shout at the children, because she seemed to shout at them a lot. Instead, she produced from somewhere on the floor of the car a multi-pack of crisps and proceeded to distribute them. She got out of the car, locked it and hurried up the steps of the café. 'I couldn't get a babysitter,' she said, 'but we won't be long, will we?'

Now that Aileen saw her mother and sister together, there was a likeness—something in the nose, the chin—that she hadn't noticed before. The four children stared in from the car, eyes fixed on their mother, aunt and grandmother. The older ones expertly ferried crisps to their mouths with small hands while the baby pulled at the teat of a bottle. Janet appeared to be expanding at the same rate that their mother was shrinking. Her sweater, one that Aileen had given her the Christmas before last, was at least two sizes too small. Janet settled herself in the chair beside her mother, directly opposite Aileen. 'How are things in London?' she said.

'Pregnant,' Aileen wanted to say, 'things in London are pregnant,' but she didn't. She wondered how Janet would react when she, in turn, learned the news; pregnancy up to now had been Janet's territory. But Janet wasn't listening for her reply. She was looking out to the car where Keith was force-feeding crisps to the baby. 'I'll crucify him,' she said, and Aileen had an image of the boy nailed to the wall outside the café, blood dripping onto the flower boxes below. Janet jumped up and banged on the glass. 'Stop it,' she shouted. Inside the café, conversation ground to a halt, but outside, the children carried on regardless. Janet ran outside, tugged at the locked car door. She felt her pockets for the keys she'd left on the café table. 'Open the door,' she screamed.

Aileen's mother looked on with the detached air of a spectator at a bullring who was waiting for the main event to start. 'She's got very fat,' she said. 'She didn't used to be that fat.'

It was then that Aileen noticed the window above their table was open. 'She'd want to watch out,' her mother said, 'or Richard will look elsewhere. I always wondered about her marrying a younger man. I worried about it.'

Aileen stood up and, too late, pulled the window shut. 'He's only three years younger,' she said.

Her mother seemed to take this as encouragement. 'Well, yes, but three years is three years,' she said, 'And he's a man. Men are different.' Their food had arrived and she took her boiled egg, began to strike it with a spoon all around the shell in sharp, brisk movements. Outside, the children had unlocked the door and now Janet was half in and half out of the car, walloping the children in turn, all of them except for the baby; walloping them with a force that made Aileen's hand go instinctively to her still-flat stomach.

Her mother took a mouthful of egg then put the spoon down. 'She used to be so pretty,' she said. 'She's let herself go.' It was true, Aileen thought, looking at her sister, Janet used to be beautiful. 'It's not easy to keep a man,' her mother continued, 'she'd want to be careful. Tidy herself up a bit.' Aileen's father had died when she was three, so it wasn't as if their mother had had to worry too long about keeping him, but Aileen didn't say this. Janet slammed the car door and began to walk back towards the café entrance.

'It's the children, of course,' Aileen's mother said, 'children do that to you.'

Janet delayed for a while in the café porch. She appeared to be studying the posters on the notice board, advertisements for local fundraisers and sports fixtures and missing pets. When eventually she returned to the table, her eyes were red-rimmed.

'You need to get Richard to have a word with that lad,' her mother said, inclining her head towards the car where Crucifixion Keith was now crying in the passenger seat. 'Otherwise he's only going to get worse.'

Aileen imagined Janet putting their mother in a hatch and running away, their mother rolled up like a rug, her head tucked into her tummy, the soft, almost noiseless thud as she landed. And then, as if they'd been discussing something different entirely, as if Janet was not sniffling furtively beside her, their mother looked across the table at Aileen and said: 'Remember those dolls you had when you were young?'

'Yes,' Aileen said. It was hard to know where her mother might be going with this.

'I was only thinking about them the other day,' her mother said. 'You were still playing with them when you were twelve or thirteen. I used to worry about that. I thought maybe you were a bit slow.'

'I collected dolls, Mam. Lots of girls did back then.'

'Yes,' her mother said, 'possibly you're right,' and she nodded, but slowly, as if even now, thirty years on, she was still not fully convinced. 'They very possibly did.'

They said goodbye to Janet and the children and left the café, driving further south until they reached Courtmacsherry and the sweep of the bay, the white fleck of waves, the boats rising and falling along the pier. There was a small public beach—a narrow strip of pebbly sand—and a hotel set back from the sea behind a line of rocks and a bank of low sand dunes. Access to the beach from the public car park was along a sloping path and Aileen helped her mother out of the car and linked her arm as they made their way down together. Her mother moved slowly and with care, her eyes following the progress of her own feet over the sand. A dozen or more elderly women were gathered at the shore, hotel residents, Aileen presumed, because they all wore matching red swim caps. They were watching an instructor, a man young enough to be their grandson, demonstrate swim strokes. And then, as though a nudge from providence, a way into the conversation Aileen had determined she would have with her mother today, she saw in the water a pregnant woman. There was something loud, almost indecent, about her large belly, as if a hologram of her impregnation were stored beneath the skin. As she made her way in to shore, a strip of seaweed drifted across her path and she flung it away without breaking her stroke. How easy she made it look, Aileen thought, how effortless. She wouldn't have been surprised if the baby had swum out of her right then, without struggle, without pain, a small, shut-eyed thing carried in on the tide like a jellyfish. 'She'd want to be careful,' Aileen's mother said. 'She's quite far along. I'd be worried about that.'

'I'm sure she'll be fine,' Aileen said. 'She seems to be a strong swimmer.'

'She's young, at least,' her mother said. 'She has that going for her. Too young, maybe. I doubt there's a husband.'

They had reached a cluster of flat black rocks. Her mother's pace was slowing, her breath coming in ever shorter gasps. Aileen looked at her and thought that she seemed to have shrunk since they left that morning. She wondered if the trip had been a mistake. But she'd asked Matron before setting out and Matron had said it should be fine, adding—rather curtly, Aileen thought—that she'd already told Janet the same thing. She helped her mother lower herself onto the flattest of the rocks to rest and for a while they sat looking out at the sea and at the elderly women who were now moving further out, yellow flotation devices tucked under their arms.

'I'm worried,' her mother said.

Aileen waited. Over the years, her mother had so devalued the currency of worry that it was impossible to guess what might come next.

'About... you know...' her mother said, 'about what will happen.'

'What will happen when?'

'You know...' her mother said, 'what will happen at the end.'

This was the first time her mother had addressed, directly at least, the fact that she would soon die. 'I'm afraid that there will be nobody there,' she said.

Aileen thought they were about to embark on a spiritual discussion, but her mother said: 'Not you, not Janet, not anybody.' Her grip tightened on Aileen's hand. 'There was a man from the ground floor died last week,' she said. 'Eily told me they couldn't find a vein in the end, and he was screeching for an hour before the ambulance arrived.'

Aileen thought of the pregnancy chat-rooms with their grotesque tales of forceps and episiotomies and thirty-hour labours. 'Mam,' she said, 'don't be talking like that. You know I'll be there.'

'You won't. You'll be in London.'

'They'll contact me when...' Aileen wasn't sure when they would contact her. Because how, at this point, could they know, really know, from one minute to the next when the end might be? 'They'll contact me when the time comes,' she said, 'and anyway, Janet will be there.'

'There's something wrong with Janet,' her mother said, 'I don't know what it is, but there's something wrong. I'm worried.'

Aileen reached across and took her mother's hand. Further up the coast, a kite surfer ploughed a white furrow through the water. Aileen followed the plume of red and orange twisting in the sky above him as if the answer, the words she needed to next say to her mother, might be found up there. They sat in silence for a while. At the end of the day, Aileen thought, this was all she and her mother could offer one another, the comfort of being frightened together.

'I noticed you had a camera back in the car,' her mother said, 'I'd like you to take my photograph.'

In the house in Ballyphehane, there had only ever been two photos of her mother: one taken on her wedding day, the other some years earlier in a cousin's drawing room when her mother was still only a girl in a gingham dress and ankle socks, hair so fiercely parted it might have been done with a knife. 'Yes, of course,' Aileen said, 'a photo would be lovely. I'll go get the camera.' She looked at her mother. 'Will you be okay here by yourself?'

'Certainly,' her mother said, 'why wouldn't I be?'

The afternoon had turned cold and as she walked, Aileen pulled her jacket tighter about her. She was passing through the dunes when a sudden dizziness struck, accompanied by the nausea that her doctor kept insisting was a good sign. She sat down for a moment and lying back on the grass she closed her eyes. Here, by the seafront, the neat lawns of the hotel gave way to scrub colonised by clusters of yellow-eyed daisies and celandines. Back in London, the father of her child—how strange those words still sounded, *her child*—would be taking the younger of his two sons to a violin lesson. He'd accused her of being heartless, selfish, in her plan to have the baby. 'The boys are six and ten,' he'd said, 'have you considered at all what this will mean for them?' The nausea worsened and she tried to still her thoughts, to breathe slowly and deeply, but was foiled by the clamour of the gulls, circling and wheeling above the dunes. Their cries were sharp and high-pitched, almost human. As she lay there in the grass, they seemed to grow louder and shriller and she sat up with a start, realising that what she was hearing was not gulls, but women.

She ran back through the dunes to discover her mother in the sea, up to her waist in water. The hotel swimmers were making their way towards her, calling to her, their red bathing caps bobbing like stray buoys as they approached. Aileen ran down the beach, sliding and stumbling over the stones. She saw her mother tumble face-forward and disappear for a couple of seconds beneath the surface. The instructor and one of the women had reached her now and were attempting to lift her, the water churning white in a mess of flailing arms and limbs. As Aileen waded out to meet them, they faced for shore and began to make their way back in, carrying her mother between them. They laid her down on the jetty wall and Aileen looked on as her mother coughed up water, spluttered, choked, coughed up some more, her hair plastered in wet strands to her skull.

They carried her mother to the hotel, up a long, straight avenue, with mature trees bordering the lawns on either side. Two peafowl, a hen and a cock, were foraging along the grass verge; they gently nudged and butted each other and raised their heads in lazy ambivalence as the party went by. Her mother was brought to a bedroom and the hotel manager organised a robe and a pot of tea. One of the women offered a change of clothes—underwear and an over-sized cardigan and skirt—which Aileen promised to return by post. Feeling nauseous again, she excused herself and went to the bathroom where she vomited a little and splashed water on her face. She came out of the bathroom to hear her mother reciting her local pedigree to the other women as if she were a stud animal, delivering it in a sing-song voice, like a poem learned at school. Aileen thought she could probably recite the list herself at this stage, she'd heard it often enough, though over the years her mother had become a little devious. Every so often, by way of erratum perhaps, or downright lie, she would slip in something hitherto unheard of, some small, brazen embellishment.

When they were left alone, her mother ran a bath, refusing Aileen's offers of help. Every so often, Aileen knocked on the door to ask if she was all right, if she needed help washing her hair, but her mother said she didn't. 'Call me when you want to get out,' Aileen said through the door. She sat in a chair by the window and watched gulls stalk the lawn outside, and a group of children play tag on the beach, moving amphibiously between pools, cliff path and rocks. After a while, she heard the gurgle of water down the plughole and pictured her mother attempting to clamber unaided from the bath, slipping on the wet floor. She went over to the bathroom, but when she put her hand to the door, she discovered it was locked.

Later that evening, back at the nursing home, Aileen got her mother into a nightdress and helped her into bed. At her mother's insistence, she went downstairs to Matron's office and fetched some brown paper to package up the borrowed clothes. 'You'll send them tomorrow, won't you?' her mother said. 'They'll only go missing here.' Eily, mercifully, hadn't yet made an appearance this evening. Aileen topped up her mother's water glass. Beside the bed was a softly rounded groove in the floorboards. They were the original boards, eighteenth-century oak according to the nursing home's brochure, and were peppered with small knot-holes that spiralled away into blackness. To the end of the bed was another, identical, groove. A different bed must once have occupied this space, its ordinances closely but not exactly mirroring the one in which her mother now lay. Some other woman, perhaps a whole series of women, had lain here, night upon night, year upon year, mouths parted slightly in sleep, all the time pressing this memento of their existence into the timber.

Her mother took a sip of water then lay back on the pillows, closing her lips tightly against the offer of more. 'You forgot to take that book last night,' she said. 'Don't forget it this time. There's nothing safe here.' And as Aileen picked up the book and put it in her bag, it occurred to her that these might very well be her mother's last words.

On the way back to her hotel, she took the slip road for Ballyphehane. Her mother's house was a modest, two-bed mid-terrace in a not-so-fashionable area, and she wondered now how Janet had managed to find a tenant for it. She parked directly outside. She would be polite, she told herself; calm and polite. The tenant—the girl—would understand; Aileen would understand if it were her. She would say that she knew it was the girl's home now, that she, Aileen, only wanted a look around, that she had come all this way. As she sat in the car, she rehearsed two speeches: one for if the girl turned out to be pleasant, the other for if she was rude. All the time she was rehearsing, she saw the girl as clearly as if she was standing in front of her, still fine-boned and blonde, still dressed like a cat-burglar.

She was about to step out of the car when she noticed that the front garden was straggling and uncared for, her mother's precious lupins listing sideways and choked by weeds. She experienced a sudden burst of anger towards the girl, who she decided now would most likely be rude. To one side of the front door an overflowing bin was disgorging its contents onto the path. The curtains were missing from the living-room window—she could imagine what her mother would say about that—and she could see beer cans on the coffee table and the silhouette of someone on the couch watching television. But the silhouette was not of a girl, fine-boned or otherwise. It was that of a man and when, perhaps having noticed the car, he stood up and came to the window, she saw that it was Janet's husband, Richard. The garden was small, no more than half a dozen yards from porch to gate, and she knew he must have recognised her. She waited, wondering if he might go to the door and invite her in, but he remained at the window and after a moment she turned the key in the ignition and drove away.

At the end of the street she went east, skirting the edges of the city as she made her way back to her hotel. Tomorrow she would say goodbye to her mother at the nursing home and would catch her flight back to London. The nausea that usually renewed its onslaught at this hour was missing this evening; her doctor had told her it would go in time, that she shouldn't worry when it did. She found that in its absence, without its bitter-sweet niggling, she felt nothing, no sense of anything beyond herself and so she tried to summon an image. All that offered itself was a grainy composite of other women's scans, a shadowy thing floating in a sea of amniotic fluid. For a moment, as she waited at traffic lights, it took on features, morphed into a girl, fair-haired and fine-boned. Its eyes were tightly shut, the way her mother's eyes had been when she came out of the water that day, steeled against the sting of salt. Her mother, who, it had seemed to Aileen, had been striking out with the last of her strength, her arms raised in resistance against her rescuers, her face set to open sea.

It Takes An Ocean Not To Break

The river's going to turn soon
I think, in your voice,
as I walk across the bridge at Richmond;
early evening, late afternoon.
Before you flew
you and I made a day to mostly window-shop.
You bought a shirt: the brightest yellow I remember.
I'm wondering how it looks on you, there,
in artificial glare,
while cyclists mount the pavement without lights,
despite it being early in the year and late in the day.

Red neon on The White Cross stares without blinking.
A barge used for puppet shows,
shut for the season, bobs in its restraints;
no children came today, nor will they tomorrow.

I've been inside for weeks.
The bedroom where I write gets too much sun:
I've kept the curtains drawn,
I couldn't tell you what the weather's been.
Work's going on.
It was bright when we walked here,
in the opposite direction, but further,
then, from Spring.

A rowing boat glides beneath my feet—
it takes four well-drilled men to edge it forward
but from here I can't tell how much they're putting in.
Their uniform broad backs in lettered vests
are a frieze of muscle memory;
do most things for long enough
the outward signs will disappear.
It looks like rain. What I'm trying to say is not to worry—
I'm just swallowing the hours.
You're still in the world somewhere in yellow;
all that unpleasantness last year's starting to seem old news.
It's gone the way you said it would when you were here.
For Christ's sweet sake, come home.

Declan Ryan

Tell Me About It

an extract

Maurice Leitch

Minding the gap they climbed out at Piccadilly, Crilly deftly threading his way along the thronged platform, Burnside trailing behind like some bemused innocent up for the day from some end of the line stop such as Cockfosters, Upminster or Ongar, and he was still pondering what life must be like in one of those deadly suburban outposts when once outside the station his guide darted straight ahead through the traffic and across to the other side of Shaftesbury Avenue.

There he stood waiting for him, a heavy-set, florid-faced figure in an open-necked white shirt and suit of old-fashioned cut, and in that instant as the cars and double-deckers roared past Burnside felt a sudden shock of recognition of something as though seeing the other for the first time, able to place him in some sort of cool, distancing perspective. Wondering what it would be like to simply turn about and dive back into the Underground again, there he dithered. The choice was his, he told himself. He could do it if he wished. He could.

But then Crilly waved across to him and the moment passed. Out of all that milling mass of humanity he, Burnside, had been singled out with a friendly gesture, and because of it he found himself crossing to the other side and the drab, facing entrance of Ward's Irish House, for, of course, he now knew where he was being taken, where else but here in the heart of the city where a frozen Eros took aim at the world and two expatriates like themselves could find the familiarity of faces far from home.

Burnside had supped in this basement den in the past, a place to catch up with those visiting writers and artists over to cadge a publisher's or a BBC cheque whilst keeping up a studied front of insolence and free-loading disdain towards their benefactors. The last time he had headed down these dark stairs a bristling duo of young Belfast poets on the literary up and up had ignored their editor to spend the entire afternoon challenging one another as to who possessed the more authentic 'Ulster voice'. Seated in the corner nursing his pint Burnside felt glad he had bailed out when he had from a place where cockerels like these two crowed over the same tiny, well-trodden cultural dungheap.

On this particular day descending the stairs he was met by the smell of bacon and boiled cabbage and remembered the Thursday lunchtime ritual of it being served to soak up the pints of stout already crowding the bar like so many dark, creamy-headed sentinels.

The place, as expected, was full, the seating arranged in four strictly designated areas around the walls of the moss-green, Art Deco-tiled room, each with the name of a Province outlined above it in curling Hibernian script.

Crilly was waving to him from the Munster section which Burnside took to be a possible clue as to his actual birthplace. But on second thoughts that sort of national sentimentality would cut no ice with his new-found buddy. No, he'd simply chosen it because that was where he'd arranged to meet 'the man', or 'the man himself', as he referred to him, as though he were some sort of demi, or semi-religious figure.

Behind him the horseshoe booth held its full complement of drinkers, thighs touching in a kind of enforced huddle, and all with the air of men with careful control of their bladder, anxious not to lose their place even if the moment arrived for them to go seeking the Gents.

'Blair! Over here!' came Crilly's breezy call, and as Burnside made his way across the uneven, flagged floor he felt conscious of eyes homing in on him from all four Provincial corners of the room, the sheer concentrated intensity of that stare unsettling, so that by the time he was halfway to the haven of Munster he was already sweating, pulling out a handkerchief to mop his brow.

Now this particular nose rag happened to be a red spotted one of the sort sporting gents of the superior classes often wear tucked into the top breast pocket of their slope-shouldered hacking jackets, or in more bohemian cases allow to limply overflow. Normally Burnside kept his thrust in a trouser pocket to anchor his change, yet nevertheless in that moment it appeared to act like a rag to a roomful of resentful bulls, branding him as someone with a tendency towards affectation, even foppishness.

Squaring his shoulders with what he hoped was a stern and manly expression he managed to join Crilly who had somehow found him a place in the snug, its table covered with pint glasses and empty plates bearing the residue of the establishment's famous traditional bacon, spuds and boiled cabbage.

'Meet Blair, everybody,' said Crilly, introducing him to the circle of stern-faced strangers. 'Runaway and refugee from the oul' sow that devours its own farrow, just like the rest of us here.'

Keenly aware of those same glances converging on him, but from close range this time, Burnside was still thinking of that accursed handkerchief, safely stowed away, of course, now but as he saw it the defining, damning image by which he would be remembered in this company. In his imagination he even heard the echo of a nickname, Blair The Hanky, or even Mister Hanky Panky, knowing how these same characters with their narrow-eyed, rural tendencies took such relish in pinning a label on somebody, for life, if need be.

And the more Crilly expanded on his credentials the more counterfeit he began to feel.

'Makin' this grand documentary, he is, for the British Broadcasting Corporation on people like ourselves over here on the mainland.'

Growing more flamboyant by the second, even his stance seemed to have taken on a larger than life dimension, unbuttoned jacket flung wide to reveal his bright red and green braces. Legs spread, thumbs tucked into those same magnificent galluses, he beamed at his listeners as though to be here in this symbolic corner of the homeland with him, Gus Crilly, had to be the ultimate privilege.

'Come, take the weight of your legs, young Blair,' he commanded and one of the group, a tousle-haired, romantic looking youth in a heavy overcoat despite the mild weather dutifully pressed himself into a corner of the booth giving him a sideways, nervous grin as he did so.

Squeezing into the space Burnside experienced a sudden warm rush towards the young guy, visualising that tattered, much-submitted manuscript burning a hole in an inside pocket of his trailing old Crombie. Once upon a time, not so long ago, either, he, too, had been like that, same embarrassed smile, reacting too fast, too gratefully to every quip and comment, no matter how boring or banal. But then some things, certain personal traits, never change. He felt like telling the young lad that and if he'd had more drink on him almost certainly would have done, slipping into the role of this wiser, much older man who'd been around the block a few times.

Then he heard Crilly enquire, 'Has T.J. been in, the man himself?' and for the first time an animated tremor seemed to ripple round the company, Burnside almost convincing himself he could feel it travelling from thigh to thigh.

One of the men said, 'I heard tell he was in town sure enough.'

'That's right,' another concurred. ' Sure if it's not London then it's Nashville or Detroit these days. Has that many irons in the fire he can hardly keep up with himself.'

Looking at the last speaker with an air of pitying condescension Crilly informed him, 'Mister, let me tell you no matter where T.J. O'Brien happens to find himself he'll always make time for an old pal.' He tapped his watch.

'Just keep an eye on that door over there, for if I know the same gent he'll be shootin' through it right on the button, pressing business or no pressing business.'

Then turning the full beam of his persuasive powers on the eager young disciple in the heavy overcoat he said, 'Dermot, ever be an angel would you and fetch a couple of oul' pints for meself and Blair here. And while you're at it get a mineral for T.J.'

He laughed.

'Him and that feckin' Pioneer pin of his. Only man in the entertainment game known to wet his whistle with nothing stronger than a Club Soda. But I suppose somebody has to have their wits about them when everybody else is out of their skulls, right?'

At this a tiny tremor of mirth ran about the gathering followed by a solemn nodding of heads as the great man and his foibles were mused upon, Burnside forming the impression a lot of this was for his benefit, for if Crilly had been the principal flag-waver to start with now the others were doing their bit to keep the parade moving smartly along. Outwardly he tried to display some enthusiasm for his coming encounter with the mighty T.J., yet still couldn't help feeling sceptical that one man, no matter how influential or charismatic, would be able to turn his fortunes around.

'If there's one individual who's the face of the comin' Ireland then T.J. is your man.'

They were on the Tube earlier and Crilly was briefing him.

'Myself now I'd put him up there alongside Eamonn Andrews, although he's far too cute to go courtin' the headlines. Somethin' of a low profile, mystery man in his own way, especially when it comes to his home life, although I have met the missus, nice homely class of a person you'd never associate with the showband or ballroom game. But then when people meet T.J. for the first time they'd never see him as a Brian Epstein or a Colonel Tom Parker figure.'

After their eager young gofer had returned with the drinks, for which Crilly made no move to pay as though the privilege of providing them with refreshment was reward enough, everyone sat staring into their glasses taking care not to allow their eyes to drift towards the entrance where their visitor was due to appear like some descending archangel in a shiny suit, mohair, possibly, even one of those lightly flecked, three-button, narrow lapelled, Italian creations.

And it did seem as though a lull had fallen over the entire place, a pensive interlude when the waves of banter and good fellowship ebb and recede, the assembled drinkers retreating into their own private worlds. Even Crilly appeared to have lost much of his customary verve.

As Burnside sat trapped there like a mute at a wake, and the hands on the Powers whiskey clock above the bar jerked inexorably towards afternoon closing-time, he started feeling more and more restless. A cramp had developed in his left calf. He felt it slowly hardening there, the size of a tennis ball. He wondered how long it would be before he cried out with the pain of it so disgracing himself and making his ignominy total.

One of the men at the table sighed deeply, tragically, and instantly the others glared at him as though he had somehow betrayed the corporate mood.

Unable to bear the atmosphere a moment longer Burnside rose to his feet, enquiring, 'Toilets?', young Lochinvar by his side pointing towards a doorway in the facing wall between Ulster and Leinster.

Making his way there Burnside couldn't help but allow his eye to lightly graze over the customers, huddled, almost conspiratorially, it struck him, in the corner dedicated to his own province. Would he recognise some of his own there, perhaps, some sort of facial familiarity striking a chord? But, alas, no, for there was that same preponderance of 'Irish skin' again, like Annabel's in Light Ent., all native Celts and G.A.A. followers to a man.

Sometimes, he reflected sadly, living over here felt as though he belonged to an endangered species, only Northern Protestant left alive, like one of those Korean pandas in Regent's Park Zoo. Perhaps they would have to import a mate for him to keep the line going, some solid, down to earth Gwen, Elsie, Netta or Roberta, with a passion for home baking and Sabbath church-going. Looking back on it he might have done a lot worse for himself instead of being drawn by the lure of those Home Counties vowels and the lingering aroma of saddle soap and tightly stretched jodphurs.

Just how predictable can one get, he was thinking in the bogs, which he had all to himself, for those first blissful, bladder-relieving minutes anyway, for suddenly the door came flying open and a figure in a ferociously stained rainproof several sizes too big for him lurched in, flapping sleeves rolled back showing reddened, emaciated wrists. To Burnside's consternation he headed for the urinal next to his, even though there were at least a dozen others to choose from. Closing his eyes and willing his own flow to accelerate, Burnside listened to the spattering noise made by the creature at his side.

But what he dreaded most was being addressed midstream. Even a comradely nod, or the merest sideways jerk of the head, was purgatory. But mercifully silence persisted and just as he was beginning to think that this time he might have managed to escape the dreaded intimacy of the pissoir, he heard his companion mutter, 'Don't remember me, do you?'

Against all his better, wiser instincts Burnside glanced sideways at the man.

'Pardon?' he said as if accidentally he had broken wind. At least it came out like that, sounding more like an apology than an actual query.

'Said you'd read my play, but never did. But then what can you expect from somebody who works for the biggest broadcasting organisation in the world?'

'Look here,' said Burnside attempting a show of authority now that he had finally managed to relieve himself, 'you seem to be confusing me with someone else, someone in the Drama department, possibly. I don't handle or deal with scripts.'

Raincoat Man appeared now to be shaking his member with more force than was customary, necessary, even, although in Burnside's own personal, out-of-the-corner-of-one-eye, across-the-porcelain divide experience, that particular finishing touch could vary from a perfunctory waggle to something infinitely more drawn out, obsessively hygienic, even, aimed at getting rid of the last distilled golden drop. Having such thoughts run through his head right now made it hard for him to concentrate on his own routine, a quick shake followed by an equally rapid zipping up.

The man in the other stall most definitely was rubbing the relic by this stage, he was, impossible to ignore it, his features having taken on an intense, almost rapt expression.

Christ, get me out of here, thought Burnside, for what could be worse than being trapped alongside some embittered scribbler jerking off? Could it be perhaps some sick new gesture of reprisal he hadn't come across before, the ultimate in critical contempt?

As he was backing out from between the walls of the old-fashioned urinal the deviant in the trailing, all-enveloping raincoat—surely another give away, a cliché, almost—muttered, 'Never bothered sendin' it back either. Or the reply coupons. Nice little earner hangin' on to peoples' few shillin's then dumpin' their life's work in an out-tray, or more likely a waste paper basket.'

In spite of everything his instincts were telling him Burnside felt he simply had to say something.

'Well, I'm really sorry you've had an unfortunate experience, but take my word for it you've got the wrong person here. I do, as it so happens, work for the Corporation, but believe me: you and I have never met before, and your script must have ended up in some other different department.'

Which is when his tormentor turned to face him, right hand buried still in the folds of his rainproof but, mercifully, at repose for the moment.

'Don't recall recordin' me a couple of months back in The Load Of Hay in Holloway, do you? Me and a bunch of the other lads? Some radio programme or other? None of us could make out what the feck it was about, somethin' about workin' on the M1, or somethin'. Never got a make for it, either, not even the price of a jar. And afterwards I gave you this big brown envelope with my play and my name and address on it, Vincent O'Malley, Flat Fourteen, Peabody Buildings, Darby Street, Lambeth. Ring any sort of a bell, does it?'

Aghast, Burnside stared at him, the entire episode a complete blank, that's if it ever existed. But why should Mackintosh Man lie about a thing like that? Holloway, he'd said. Certainly it had the right ring to it, the sort of area he might have trawled for his contributors. Victims, he almost caught himself thinking.

But all that seemed such a long way off now, all those captured voices circling in some sort of electronic limbo, and, of course, he had to face the fact, almost certainly now lost forever except in the memory of the actual people involved, like this demented creature confronting him and, it would seem, playing with himself once more under his terrible old Burberry.

But then in a development chilling in the extreme, this, well, this wanker, moved rapidly across the tiled floor to the door blocking his, Burnside's, escape.

'Listen, listen,' he hissed, 'there's these three country fellas in a bar, right? As well as the landlord bloke. Out in the West some place. Sligo, or Leitrim, maybe. A dark and stormy night, and they're tellin' each other stories, ghost stories mostly, and then this young woman comes in, a stranger from Dublin, just bought a house in the area. Well, of course, your boul' lads are all out to impress the same blade and maybe scare her as well, and the yarns get more and more outrageous and eerie, fairy bushes and graveyards and knocks at midnight, stuff like that.

But here comes the clincher, the young woman has a story of her own, and this one happens to be true, you get me, about her own daughter and a terrible drownin' and a warnin' beforehand, and it shuts the lads up full time.

And, well, that's about it. Maybe the end could do with a bit of polishin', I don't know, but I'm open to suggestions. You might say it's about people lookin' back and wonderin' where it all went wrong. But it's not all tragedy and gloom, I've put in a few odd laughs as well.'

There followed a lengthy pause broken only by the hiss from the water cistern high up on the wall. Burnside's brain had temporarily shut down while the other rattled on, his gaze drawn instead to the back of the door and the biro and penknife art-work there on display from others with their own message like the man now holding him captive, the mildest, least offensive being *Up Tipp* and *God Bless Dev*, although there were a couple of lovingly executed renderings of *Fuck The Queen* and a deeply incised *Ian Paisley Is A Cunt* which made him feel even more like some innocent bystander who had somehow wandered into a foreign war zone.

'So what you reckon then?'

An almost plaintive note had entered the other's voice and suddenly Burnside felt an unexpected trickle of compassion. Sad, sad bastard, he thought, hugging that hopeless play of his like it was his firstborn—most probably, it was, too—oblivious, or not wanting to see it for the poor deformed defective it truly was.

But just as he was on the point of perjuring himself, saying something like, 'certainly there's some dramatic potential there,' or, 'I'm sure with the right cast, you just never know,' the door swung in, banging into the would-be playwright, who stumbled forward, a look of shock and desperation on his face.

Behind him, framed there, stood Crilly grinning knowingly as though taking in the situation at a glance.

'I hope, Vinnie, you're not botherin' my friend here with your usual oul' bollocks. Can a bloke not have a piss in peace without you tormentin' him?'

Retreating to the sanctuary of the wash-hand basins the man in the raincoat stared at him, all his earlier bravado replaced by an expression of dread.

'You know if you keep trailin' blokes into the bogs people will maybe start thinkin' you're just, well, a wee bit on the, well, you know what I mean…'

Then, turning to Burnside, he briskly announced, 'T.J.'s just been on the blower. Change of venue, but we're definitely on. Ready to roll, are we?'

Absolutely, Burnside was thinking in a relieved rush, making his delayed move for the door with its record of God knows what festering spites and rancours, most of it aimed personally at himself, he had decided, for daring to enter this citadel of resentful Irishry in the first place. And ushering him back along the dark, damp-smelling passageway beyond, Crilly appeared in agreement.

'That bunch of literary losers back there'll be goin' on about Kafka or Kierkegaard any feckin' minute. All with a novel or some kind of a book inside them. Where it's goin' to remain, believe you me. Like that poor eejit in the jakes. I suppose he button-holed you about his masterpiece, did he? Ever hear such a load of oul' tripe in your puff? Three blokes and some dozy bird in a bar tellin' one another ghost stories. I ask you, who in their right mind would ever want to pay god money to go to see the like of that? No, you don't want to go recordin' any of that crowd. Only brought you here to meet T.J. Anyway, not to worry, we're off to catch up with him at Kilburn Park. Some class of a publicity shoot for his new group. I did mention he's a big band promoter, didn't I, among a lot of other things?'

But if he had, the information had coursed over Burnside like a breaking wave leaving no trace save the sensation of being buffeted by a succession of more and more conflicting instructions and commands.

'There's a quiet back way out of this place not a lot of people know about.'

Being led along another passage even darker and more dust-laden than the first Burnside felt grateful he hadn't got to brave all those stares in the bar a second time. Like being scrutinised on your first day at school and found wanting. Still he did feel a trifle apprehensive at the prospect of meeting and recording the legendary T.J., sounding, as he did, like someone used to steering any interview his own way. And he suspected it might well turn out to be an 'interview', as opposed to the kind of free-wheeling encounter he was used to.

Like A Fish Needs A…
Joanna Walsh

> 'Always carry a repair outfit. Take left turns as much as possible.
> Never apply your front brake first.'
> —Flann O'Brien, *The Third Policeman*

It's something to do with my cycle. That's what I'll tell the doctor. I'll say I think there's something wrong with my mind. I've read it, about women, didn't want to believe it, but I guess there's some truth in every cliche. Didn't T, who I'd met on a non-date at the Tate, say, 'There's a week every month when women go crazy'?

I didn't want to contradict him at the time: I was interested. Yes, I was offended but, unchallenged, what he'd told me turned in my mind. He'd arrived on his bike. I'd taken the tube. The doctor has given me forms to fill. The date led to… nothing.

T had a minotaur physique, spare as the iron seat and handlebars of Picasso's Bull's Head (we saw it in a touring exhibition along with Duchamp's readymade rear-wheel spinning singly in mid-air). I saw T's chest once: two round hard plates with… cleavage! A definite gap. That's what you get from all that cycling. I usually go for scholarly types, had never felt anything like it on a man before.

The next time he arrived panting, having cycled up Haverstock Hill to meet me at the Freud museum. I didn't see his bike. He said he'd parked it round the corner. I showed him mine once. A BSO he called it, a bike-shaped-object: looks like a bike, but isn't. 'Suppose I see a bicycle,' said T, quoting philosopher John Searle. 'In such a perceptual situation there is a distinction between the object perceived and the act of perception. If I take away the perception, I am left with a bike; if I take away the bike, I am left with a perception that has no object, for example, a hallucination.'

My bike was far away, in a different city, though I rode it to the station, as I did every day.

It's a man's bike. Once I had a woman's cycle but only briefly, in the last months of pregnancy, to triangulate my round scoop of belly. I'm over that now, stepped over it, stepped through. As soon as I stopped bearing, I gave it up, gave it away, can't remember what I did with it. A man's bike—if I can't ride it pregnant, I won't get pregnant. Now there's logic for you.

Many of the objects in the Freud Museum were labelled: quite ordinary objects with extraordinary labels. The violets in the toilets were labelled 'rape' which, in French, is 'viol' and, leant against their pot, a card saying how a mention of the flowers in French had led Freud down a byway into someone's unconscious. Bike words are often French, because of the Tour de France I guess. When someone mentions a bike, said Freud, there must really be a bike, or the idea of a bike, acting on the person's neurones, which are purely physical.

Consciousness is physical, and even the idea of a bike is a thing: perception cannot have no object. The violets were displayed in the women's lavatory.

A bicycle is double: two wheels for balance, bipedal, mirrored handlebars, one light in front and one behind suggesting that wholeness is a co-joined two. But no one kisses in the Freud Museum. No one is coupled. It's a place for groups: schoolkids giggle, earnest friends tour in threes and fives; there are families even, only never what causes them.

And, in his study, there's a picture of Freud riding a bicycle. No not riding, but posing with, as though about to leave, and not at the start of a journey— stopped somewhere looking like mid-way. Who are the others he is with? And where, in Hampstead, did Freud park his bike?

*

If a fish needs a bicycle, don't drink like one: that's sound advice. If you do, you'll end up outside the station late at night, drunk, cold, fumbling the lock with numb fingers then, next morning, wrecked, frame stripped down to derailleurs and jockey wheels. It won't be good. For either of you.

Still it's inviting: the bicycle seat, warm negative of a… negative. The leather saddle nub's white-stitched ridge, polished and brown, slips neatly between. A good feeling. It can lead you to let go of the brakes. That thing men do that I could never: ride a bike on the level with hands free, hips thrust forward to steer. I've tried, but I don't have the balance, the centre of gravity. This time, once again the cogs turned over like bones in their sockets, crunched—dislocated—the gears' vertebrae. When you fall off, get straight back on, they say. But too much freewheeling leads only downhill. It's a vicious cycle.

Next morning I noticed my saddle's leather was split, and from its gash spilled tiny white beads suspended in a sort of gel, white patches on my skirt, brushed absently; more patches, dried, on my inner thighs. Otherwise, trailing my left arm to the elbow, a bacon of road rash—tyre tracks got I don't remember how.

So, ticking the boxes here in the surgery, my bike lashed to a lamp post outside, I'm trying to be more balanced—as to the questions, and also as to the world-shaped-object which may exist entirely as I don't perceive it. It seems wrong, despite what I've perceived as corresponding to physical reality, to tick every extreme. It seems wrong not to balance one answer with another, when it might just an imbalance in my cycle.

Through the doctor's window, set high in the wall as much to exclude thoughts of outside as to shield passers-by from the unwell, I glimpse a man crouched over a hybrid with the spine of a rabbit, a *danseur*, dancing on the pedals. It must have been T, cycling away.

monologue for cabman

Kevin Barry

avenue to gillingham close – i cut my hand by leytonstone high road –
come around the close earlshoff road – i was opening a can of drink – the
blood splatters and the blood is all over – a vicious hot summer day
coming into evening the window is rolled and the arm is out and the blood
in tiny drips spatters the jesus out of matcham road – driplets or droplets
– to the high road – go selby road – by the plough and harrow to langthorne
road – by the st patricks rc – the cut is after taking a slice from the inside
of my thumb – oh mother – and it sings is the only way to put it – the high
pitch note a sharp cut pain has – the longest evening of the summer and
this year – the eyes are watering inside my head – all i can do is carry the
tune of the cut under my breath as i go – hello – this frail arm raised for
me – this old dear she waits for me – hello – veined in the eyes – carrying
a bag of bottles – clinkety clink she like her drink – a talker right off i take
her for – a talker – says she, this is brutal heat and seven o clock in the day
– no respite, missus – and it is worse it's getting she says – she is irish from
a long time ago – as myself – beet to the heels off the ox mountain county
sligo now this is a big boned boy and handsome was how my mother
would say for the fattish child i was – she says – the old dear – she says
there's a show tonight in hackney i'd pay good money to see – the empire,
i says? – no she says the dog and feathers joe malone from kiltimagh – in
the county of mayo i says – beautiful singer she says the tears'd stream
down your face and the heart would give out on you and which way you
taking me for dunedin road anyhow, driver – by the leyton library, i says
– that'll do, she says, come up ruckholt road – exactly i says – i were
propositioned once, she says, in the leyton library – that weren't today nor

yesterday, I says – cheeky, she says, he was an indian gentleman he had lovely knees – knees? i says – it was summer it was shorts he was in lovely… brown… agreeable… knees – steady, love, i says – very agreeable gentleman, she says, handsome as a dove – steady, i says, or shall i open another window, dear, get some air in – cheeky, she says, anyhow i had cyril at home and he's wanting his tea since the legs went he's useless for himself can't heat a tin of beans – what's happened cyril and his legs, i says – he's fallen out a window, she says – nasty, i says – ground floor, she says, not like it was sky breaking news but he's done himself in well enough leg-wise – the hand slips in the bag the screwing of the cap the little nip she takes, like a bird – so it's not like i can run away to mumbai she says not with cyril at home wanting his beans – wouldn't be just, ma'am, i says – he was trying to adjust the drapes on the runner, she says, he was always a holy fool was cyril – anyway, she says, this was… what, she says, 1976 – montreal olympics, i says – pig heat that summer and all, she says – i tell you now exactly where i was i says i was on a moped i was learning my routes i was straight off the ox mountain plonk me down in piccadilly circus you could have told me it was the face of the yellow moon – i don't sleep so hot if there's a moon, she says – i've come down adelaide road the one-way – i know how you feel, love, i says, on the full moon nights, i says, what i haven't seen in the back of this cab – go on, she says – oh i have seen the nuttiest things, i says, i have seen a notorious midget from kentish town attempt to sell chinese cultural artefacts to a vicar from the city of lagos in nigeria, he's anglican by the collar – now, she says – and i wouldn't mind, i says, but when the vicar won't buy, the midget, he comes over shirty – they can do, she says – no call for shirty, she says – but here, she says – are you sure, she says… are you sure it was a midget? – how'd you mean, i says – sometimes she says sometimes what you take for a midget can be a jockey – hmmmm, i says – here we go, i says, dunedin road – still my blood sings and drips and the air above and the sky thickens the summer even at its height is turning – orient way temple mills depot and the hackney marshes – she don't want to tell me a midget from a jockey – i know a jockey – how many years have i carried the fancy how many times charing cross station for kempton park? – my hands could do it and my eyes closed – nose bring me there by the feel even – midges about and all – thick in the air – midges, midgets – the words go skewy and all over at the rough end of a nine hour shift – i had a jockey try have it off with his missus or ladyfriend back of this cab one time – i said, here – i said, give over now – i said what you do in the sanctity of your own bedroom, that's a private and blessed business, and the best of luck to you with it all, but let's not, friend, not here, not in the light of day, not with the traffic heavyish – chatsworth road is having one of its dreary moments – it can do – i wouldn't mind she was a blonde about six foot two – i'll take clifden road for churchill walk – there's a regular there wants taking from churchill walk – poor sam – poor sam's my old greek lad – he is originally green lanes – he's taught me a bit of greek has sam as it happens – here he comes now, the long face on, that'll be his tomatoes he's worrying about – he's taught me that hasappis means butcher – in the greek – and malaka means wanker and what more would you need, i says, in this line of business, and sam got a laugh out of that and it's not often sam gets a laugh in – hello sam – well, he says, the latest, he says, these toms, he says – it's a write-off, tony, he says, it's the disaster season we've always known was coming – now this is a man who is quite frankly obsessed with his blooming tomatoes – he says, first they've bolted and now they've got the yellow wilt – nasty, i says, and i wince for him in the rear-view – knowing sam and his toms this twenty years gone the last words you want to hear from the poor man's mouth is yellow and wilt – they've a thirst on now, he says, and there is not a sea that would quench it   the trail of blood is microscopic or so i imagine and you could not see it with the naked eye but maybe you could sense it from high up if there was a sensor above the sky that mapped by the heat of our blood these trails we take all over the town say that there are tiny red dots to mark on the map the heat of our blood as we move all over the town – pedro st to redwald road – and the river – the lea – for the air of a river the word is riverine – its atmosphere or trapped feeling – sam the greek he says the worst thing that can happen in the line of tomatoes is if they've come in too soon – like much in life, sam, i says – patience, i says, is the virtue required but sam is not for talking, not tonight, the year is screwed on sam if his toms have come in early, and watery, this summer there will be no alignment of the stars for sam – i am thinking of love by st john-at-hackney-gardens – in fact i am no longer married to doreen – good luck sam i says but he hardly has the eyes up from his trainers tonight poor sam and his toms though he adds the usual tip his twenty per cent never let it be said for the old boy from green lanes – a gentleman, one of the sad – i believe he tried to do away with himself one time but did not follow through – he wouldn't have that kind of show in him – hot as it is the year is turning the grasses yellowing it comes around us quick the turn of year and a quiet, an eerie hour can creep down on you out of nowhere and the sky and nothing and the road just slides up of its own volition and eats away the last of the daylight for its darkness – the exasperating fact is that despite all my best efforts – the gymnasium? the twenty mile sunday hikes? the bloody pilates? – i aged quicker than doreen – dalston lane by the three compasses – and for all those years and monday nights – our nights out – i'm sat with her – in bistro or in bloody wine bar – and i'm thinking i could do better, you know, they'll take her for my mother or for an auntly type but then, one dark sudden morning, i wake up, i look across the pillows, and doreen, at fifty-three years of age, an april morning, is fresh as a watered plant, she is positively girlish, and me, i've turned into the most horrendous old bum-face – into my father, essentially – face like the sole of a farmer's boot and the back of my head so wide you'd play handball off if – sat in my cab with a breezeblock on for a noggin – i'll keep going tonight – sandringham road by the argos – an argos always reminds me of doreen – it is as well that i let the streets eat me up tonight – my mother would always say if you have morbid thoughts the thing to do is stay busy – and this was a woman who never stopped going – this was a woman who'd be ironing sheets at four in the morning – tonight i'll let the streets eat me up and chew me down and spit me out again – the town is filling up with its people and lights – and i have a bad five minutes re: the doreen situation – it is when you see people who are young and alive – i get an unpleasantness rising up in me sometimes – a sourish feeling – in the vicinity of balls pond road – balls pond road to essex road by the hope and glory – i haven't taken a drink in fourteen years – i'd have been on the soda water in the wine bars with doreen and doreen acting glamorous on white rioja – and i do not wish to sound odd nor superstitious nor sectionable nor in any way batty but there are secret forces beneath these streets and they send up their airs and dark energies – we might as well be out in the open about this – beneath the streets and tar – upper street the stations of the cross the stations of my life – and these airs or feelings might be made of a sorrow or sadness that has lingered for years in a place or has been trapped there – i'll pick it up clearly sometimes as i drift past and i can smell from a great distance off danger in the night – the word for the atmosphere of wolves on the air should be wolverine – a blessed arm rises for me and thanks be to jesus that it does before i go off again down that dark tunnel and into those black thoughts – wolves – hello, she says, i'm for the bohane gardens but take it easy, driver, and take it nice and slow, coz i've had a bit of a feed tonight – mr ottolenghi has done very well for himself, i says – what that man can't do with a chickpea, she says – immense, i says, and he's a perfect gent and all – and we drift together and banter and we move – and the air of the city moves through its night graces its warm embraces its secret traces its melancholy faces its dank its dark and hidden places and all of its motley races and all of its nutjobs and all of its hard cases – by clondesley place i am almost light-hearted – her words – she tells me of her life and loves – her words and scent fill up the cab – her dramas – and how it is the secret in life to remain at all times cheerful – i couldn't agree more, missus, i says – miss, she says – and our eyebrows rise together to meet in the rear-view – hello – i give her my card and my heart is going like the two-thirty at kempton park over hardish ground – often it's around here i'd be, i says, often it's around this patch of the woods for me, i says, should you find some night that a cab is hard to find – thank you, she says – and she taps the number into her phone under cabbie, brackets, irish, with an x alongside – cheeky – and she gives the card back to me – copenhagen street – cartwright gardens – i was young around here one time – friday nights i'd meet doreen by goodge street station – tottenham street, again, second time today – ghosts of fitzrovia – the cut sings and i bite through the new scab and there is blood, again – riding house street for charlotte street for

Number One Haircut In Town

Work means routine. Black tea
and oranges before ten, lunch
at the cafe near the Masonic temple.
Or maybe a haircut, the same place
for how many years now?
A cheap barbers, on the edge of Soho
its tacky Theatreland masquerade:
the photos of Kirk Douglas
in Paths of Glory, Marilyn Monroe
before she caught the final bus.
Show posters and flyers, actors
sometimes spilling out from auditions
to trim thespian beards. Always
staffed by the peripatetic and those
who have drifted here to remain.
The Spanish girl, who saddened
when she mentioned how long
she had worked here. Another
I saw only once, who handled clippers
as though she was shearing sheep.
The boy with tattoos and glasses,
who spoke of his pregnant girlfriend,
but would, later, become evasive
when I asked about the child.
I had forgotten about this other girl
until she appeared again, after
four or five years. I could recall
the smiles some men would flash
when she called for the next person
in line. Her beauty is still intact
but a disappointment haunts it now,
a regret. Did she feel that she
had left this place for a better life?
I am a swift customer these days,
my head shaved rather than groomed.
Afterwards, she takes payment, her gaze
already turning to the next in line:
these steps we make into the future
only to find ourselves marooned.
On the walk back, late for work,
in the crowds around Seven Dials,
I see myself in a car window:
a fleeting man, slightly harried
surprised to find myself even here.

Daniel Bennett

Downstream
Sean O'Reilly

Dropped out of the sky into Dublin for the day. Press some flesh in Georgian rooms because I'm here on business don't you know. Admire a skirted rump or two just long enough for them to see. This is Capel Street now, the sun on my face. And that strange coolness at the back of my neck because I've just had the rug trimmed. Halt at a junction waiting for their new tram to pass. She's a pretty machine. With bells on. Infinite are the ways it could have happened but who comes borne by behind glass, a private smile, seated like royalty, only the Redzer. We lock eyes. There's the gurrier's wink from her and this numbskull in a new suit forgets years of everything.

Now I'm not spoofing or making noises about being a stud but I could rise to any occasion for that chick. Indoors or out, down in the dumps or in bits after midnight. Sure remember the time in Huddleston Road and the gas leak, the entire street was supposed to be evacuated and where were we?

She had our Hughie on tap. Those little fingertips at my throat. The lightness of her nudity on my back. I need cock mister every kiss said. The tits, the beefy freckled balubas she loved to lick herself. Right from the first time ever on a mattress on the floor of the Stamford Hill squat to the final sayonara in a power shower in Ally Pally, me pretending I couldn't hear her crying, I never let the girl down. That's a distance of twenty odd years we're talking. Though the Redzer was never one for looking back.

Do you mind the time we hit Cornwall for the weekend? I'd say or something. You got all hot and bothered by the young dudes in the wetsuits. Remember? Phase two, this was, about two weeks in. We were living in—

Hughie, can we not just watch this film without you competing with it? And haven't I told you this phases talk of yours ruins my mood. This phase. That phase. It depresses me. Life put in boxes like that. Stacked and labelled in one of your smelly boss's misery-brown removal vans.

Remember the peacock feathers back at the hotel? You nicked them out of a fat bronze vase and did the seven veils. You were up on the window sill in your yellow knickers. Remember the day we bought those knickers together in that creepy wee shop near Paddington?

Neither of us knew it then but there would only be three phases. The first was six-and-a-half weeks long, then we did a line for five months, and lastly, the big one coming in at just under two years. Three stints together ended by three ladylike disappearing acts. That girl could do one out of your life quicker than it takes to boil the kettle.

Where you going?

I told you.

Tell me again.

Stop sniffing my bra Hugh. Give it to me now.

You have magic powers so you do. I wasn't in the mood there, right, and then I realised you were standing behind me, close up behind me, dead still, and I pretended I didn't know you were there, and I could hear your breathing getting deeper, and I started to feel it going into my back from you, waves of it and—

Baloney. Why do we always have to talk about it afterwards? Now give me my bra or you'll never see these again, she said, with a priceless shoulder shake.

Or take that vintage scene of rattling through the tunnels under north London. There'd been a few days of full-on battles about the move back to Ireland. Throats raw, we went down into the tube at Angel. Normally, you don't catch me underground but this Sunday morning I followed her down, probably because I thought she was punishing me. And I was getting a taste for it. The escalators were out of order. We seemed to have the tiled rabbit holes to ourselves. Deeper and deeper ahead of me she sank. Left me alone with the fear. The characters in those posters for musicals and plays all stopped having fun and stared out at me, licking their lips. On the third escalator a thick banshee fog of ventilated air set the stage for my comeuppance. Then down the last few steps on my arse, holding my nose. The way the train just about made the fit between the platform and the concave cliff, squeezing in slower, slower, then stuck.

There was Viv, her hair down now, stepping bravely on board. The carriage was empty. Of course it was. Because it was doomed. People knew not to get on. And had I really seen a driver? There was no driver. It was Tony Blair's fault. The blood on his hands. Innocence can get you killed anytime. Yes, they were trying out a new type of time-bomb called Innocence. We had stumbled into some kind of classified trial run. The cliff-sized ads rippled as the train doors hissed and banged against Viv who had put her body in the way. The look she gave me meant act normal Hughie or they'll eradicate us and she hoisted her blouse and bra and stepped back into the carriage.

Those anti-authoritarian tits did what the meds or the counsellor couldn't fix. She sat me down, knelt between my legs. Ripped off the belt like a shackle. The zip like a gag. Lights blinking. Grey roots in the red furze. That nose of hers had definitely been straightened. She had you emptied by Moorgate.

The Wee Red liked a drink and a joke and a vigorous tête-a-dick when piqued but she never enjoyed hearing me tell the story of how we met. And met again eleven years later. And met again two years hence. Everybody else saw the funny side of it. And the scary side of how your life can take a surprise turn while you're crab-walking towards a Camden kebab shop or wolf-whistling a bird in south London. Infinite are the ways we might not be ourselves. One small decision, a detour or an extra few minutes in the sack and you might be somebody else. And somebody else might be you instead. The Redzer didn't dig the message. As a matter of fact, I was giving one of my better renditions of it, our story, the last time I saw her miffed freckly bake, when she walked out of a tapas bar on Green Lanes where our mates had gathered to wish us the best of luck on our move back to Ireland. They were mainly my crowd as it turned out, all except one, Sally, a Bollywoodish lab-technician who Viv had been messing about, and with, not quite behind my back. Only Sally and me mid-flow, noticed her leave. That was our Viv for you, always slipping away before the punch line.

I said to her, Sally, I feel your pain, girl. She's walked out on me not once but twice and there wasn't a whore small or cruel enough in London to take my mind off her. Back in the 80s, right, during our first phase, you know what she said to me, and right, she was holding her asshole open with both hands at the time, no fancy nail polish then either, seventeen she was, a runaway, and she says, Do me Hughie like I'm Thatcher. Maggie Thatcher. I'd never heard the like.

Sally, down unlocking her bike, said, Somewhere in your moronic heart I think you know Genevieve doesn't want you to go with her. You try so hard to embarrass her because you know this. She wants to be free.

You're being a sore loser, Sally girl. She was scot-free twice and she still came back. And why's that do you think? Because of my skill in the kitchen?

Don't you get it? She thinks she has damaged you.

You know your problem Sally. You take her too seriously. This is where you went wrong. Irish women like to say whatever the fuck they want and then expect you to forget it ever happened. You're way too heavy. You're too—remember that night the three of us did our bit for love together? Me at the top and you at the bottom? Who was the one who got all upset and weepy afterwards? Who was the one who comforted you? Me. Not Viv. You need to lighten up.

Pussy to the saddle, she said, I would hurry home if I was you.

Viv and me had another fight before coming out. She was right in my face. I pushed her away and she hit her head off the door frame. It was the excuse she needed. How dare you hit me? I didn't hit you. How dare you hit me? I walked the plank of shuttered Green Lanes. The key turned without the usual resistance.

In the hall, a recent blast of Givenchy corrupting the damp air. Light on in the bathroom and the living room. Her green coat should be over the back of the chair, her bag on the table. She should be in bed, a little drumlin under the duvet. You don't even have to check for the suitcase she keeps in the spare room. You found the ring under your pillow.

Stop lying Hughie. You don't want to go.

I do want to. I'm ready for a change.

I know you don't want to go. I know okay. It's obvious. So can you just stop lying about it. Just tell me.

All because I've had a few?

You're coked up. You're out boozing all the time. Just face it will you. You haven't even found the balls to tell Tobias yet, have you?

It's called having mates. I'm saying goodbye to my mates.

Just say you've changed my mind. I can take it.

Maybe you're the one who's changed their mind. Maybe you want to do another runner. How many fresh fucking starts does one woman need?

We all think about it at some stage, moving back home for good. The jolt of the touch-down on the Dublin tarmac that will finally realign the bones and exorcise those phantom pains. For some it's the death of kin with a plot of land or your own kid giving you lip in a squaddie's tongue, and some run out of excuses one fine day and pack their bags in a hurry. A voice inside which you normally treat as a crank suddenly makes sense while you're doing the shopping. Or after one last attempt to wreak havoc in your life, the voice falls silent. If you can survive that, London, or wherever it is, becomes your castle. I'd say it should be a recognised condition. And the nearest I came to it was with Genevieve Querney from the cramped streets of Fairview by the Liffey swells.

So why didn't I kill her that night on the bus back from Brixton? Why didn't I smash every tooth in her two-timing head and plop her juvenile's butt in the Thames? For weeks, months, she'd been filling my shell-like with her arguments for calling it a day in London. What a heartless city it was, so indifferent and rude, so many hours wasted on transport, where the pound is king and the pollution hides the taste of violence, the racism and the rent, the multicultural myth and meanwhile she's munching on home counties' best Bollywood promise. On the way back from that flop of a Morrissey gig was the moment she chose to fess up. All her guff about Ireland maybe, or the rain sealing us in on the top deck by the front window, had me telling her about the day I left Dublin on the ferry, and how I fell in with this German couple. Rainbow warriors roasted by decades of bonfires who took a shine to young Hughie on his big break for freedom. Who incited him with drink and kindness and bloody tales of the battle of the Beanfield in 1984 when the pigs had given the New Agers a lesson in authority at the solstice gathering in Stonehenge. Who took him below to the hold and laid him out in the back of the camper van and said they would cleanse him for his journey and they put their hands on him and pinned him down with whispers and Poor Hughie began to freak. He pulled his new flick-knife and pierced the husband's thigh. He got out the driver's door, ran for the stairwell and spent the rest of the trip like a stowaway on the misty deck.

I'm sleeping with somebody else, said the Redzer.

You bet you are, I agreed. I'm a different person now. And it's all your doing actually. Mind that shy wee bloke you made take off his clothes? You had to do everything. I couldn't even get my desert boots off. You know I never knew it existed, not for real, not for the likes of me. Beauty, I mean.

I'm having sex with another woman Hugh.

That one Genevieve's tastes were always changing. Any hint of a routine in the bedroom and you'd notice she was talking more about other countries again, about the places she had never seen. Phase three, Ally Pally, she had less of the multiple O's but they were deeper, and more serious, and paralysing, and lasted for minutes on end. I used to have to check she wasn't deceased. A far cry from the days of phase one when she couldn't keep her hand out of her Yellow-Pack knickers. Or the woman of phase two who had discovered silk and white gloves and liked to stand on my head.

Tell me you never stopped looking for me.

Never. Every day.

And you couldn't get it up for anyone or I'll crack your skull.

Nobody gives me the horn like you. My meat was broke. Girls and boys too—I tried everything.

Baloney.

I knew I'd track down your gee again. Didn't I find you?

The boys and me in the van, coming down by Ruskin Park in Camberwell, winter, 2003, after a job. The traffic slow because of road works so we cut over to Denmark Hill. Tall houses behind wet bare trees on a steep slope. Spotting a bit of skirt skidding on the mowldy leaves, I stick my head out the window and shout, Get your tits out Ginger, show my gob for the reaction, and catch a face smile and wink back at me. We drive on for a few minutes before it sinks in and I tell them to pull over.

Put me down you big yob, she says in a shower of greasy drops from the high boughs.

We repaired to the nearest pub, right by the overground station there. Hair shortened to bob length again, a black cashmere turtle neck, no make-up. Two years since she absconded from Tufnell Park. She had got herself a new passport and cleared off to Estonia to teach English again. And now she was back living south of the river for the first time. I couldn't help wondering who it was she might have left killing a vodka in Tallinn after he'd gone for a dump and came back to find her gone.

What do we do? she asked after a long silence. She seemed shaken, awestruck by us meeting again.

Did I really believe it when I said, We're not trapped in a lift or something Genevieve. We don't have to do anything. We can walk away if we want. Was it not already decided, eye meeting eye on Denmark Hill? Wasn't I already imagining one of her specialities, the pitter-patter of her tiny fingers up and down my shaft, the muscly international tongue?

She took my hand across the table, and said, Hugh I'm sorry, and I'm just not at all.

A few massive days later, Tobias invited me for a frame or two in the club in Soho. When he wanted a serious word, it happened over a game, an elder spider crawling over the walnut edges of the table on a nest raid, jabbing, retreating, the white horseshoe moustache twitching under the upholstered Stanfast shade. He plays like he's against the clock, fast, instinctual. I've seen him do a one-four-seven in eight minutes ten seconds with his extra-heavy black and gold ash cue. If the old man had got wind already that the Redzer and me were rubbing shoulders again, he might find another use for it.

By the time the reds were down, he was still talking business. Around then Tobias was pondering expansion into the specialist art stuff, transporting gear between galleries and exhibitions. I fluffed an easy take of the yellow.

You're not even here, he said. No concentration. No focus.

Late night, boss.

The reason you got out of the van, what, this claustrophobia of yours again?

He was on to us. I looked around and saw that the other eight green slabs were empty. I could have sworn there were games underway when we arrived. You don't lie to Tobias. I've seen where that can lead a man. Anyway, I owed him. He'd put me back together so many times the man could write the instructions.

It's a small world, I said.

Don't try to be smart, son. That Irish dick of yours is happy only when it's dipped in trouble, he said, straightening his monographed cuffs. Dip it somewhere else. The Chinese. The blacks. Try the Brazilians. Those women could teach her a thing or two about her issues with authority.

She's all of those in one.

He uttered some Yiddish oath and said, Correct me if I'm wrong here son but didn't I hear lately that you had been discovering, what shall we call it, a new predilection for the more epicene arts of Greek street?

Dumbly, I watched him smoothing the moustache, a sign he was aggravated.

Third time lucky maybe, I said.

Time you say? Time is our element. Each of us moving through time. At high speed. What have I taught you?

Rivers to the sea. I know. Rivers to the sea.

Well stop behaving like an effing salmon then.

Not so long after that, Viv came home and said she had bumped into Tobias on the street near her work. Typically, she refused to believe there could be any other explanation for him being in the area than stalking her. No, he hadn't said anything directly but he had insinuated plenty, she claimed. All his melancholy pleasantries added up to a threat. He's only your boss, Hughie. He employs you to organise moving boxes around in an ugly van. I let the jibe pass. I wanted to keep the peace because this was the day before the anti-war protest in 2003. Viv was going on it while I had made sure to be as far away as I could, out at Heathrow dealing with some missing cargo. We seemed to have agreed to avoid any mention of it this time around. No calls or texts from her during the march either. The news on the airport screens showed it was colossal. In the evening, on the way to join Tobias and some of the lads at our usual spot, a Chinese on Brewer Street, there were towers of placards in Soho Square and skeleton costumes were doing victory dances from the lampposts over the hyped up crowds.

The biggest in history, Viv said with a drum-roll on the table when she appeared in the restaurant. Tobias plucked his moustache, probably thinking I had tricked him. The others had gone on thankfully. Viv treated the two of us to noisy kisses on the mouth and then she slid in beside Tobias. After a while, he ordered her the Peking Duck because she was too busy with the day's highlights to read the menu. Then she scoffed the whole lot of it without noticing, the steam from the pancakes melting the face paint. Hoarse, euphoric Genevieve didn't give a monkey's. She didn't miss a beat either when Tobias, after dipping the corner of his napkin in a water jug, began to gently wipe the smears of paint and hoi-sin sauce from the corner of her mouth.

From all the reports the turnout in Dublin and Paris and Berlin and everywhere else had been huge also. Every generation discovers the secret anew, Viv needed us to understand, the secret the establishment works to blind us to with hourly blizzards of fear and hatred and envy and self-disgust and the massive trap of the unending present. And that secret is our power together in numbers, she said, looking hard at each of us in turn, her voice so tired now she was almost gasping. Yes, the grinning tyrant Blair was finished. The pseudo-battle between left and right was over. This is the new dawn, you two dopes, don't you see?

Infinite are the ways this could run, I was thinking, ready to jump in if there was a barney. To give him his due though, Tobias, who's the kind of Tory who believes people would eat their own children if you let them, encouraged her to keep talking, tempted perhaps to bask in the rays of hope from her. I suppose he'd never seen this side of The Redzer. Or her, his solemn way of listening and questioning that gradually made you realise there was even more to what you were trying to say than you thought.

A few hours in and the two of them had more or less forgotten my presence across the manky purple tablecloth. That was a sweet feeling. A wee quiet harbour in the corner of a Soho restaurant. Soppy as it sounds, I was able to kick back with my Courvoisier and behold the two people who meant the most to me in the world bobbing together briefly on the current that pushes all things towards the sea of tranquillity.

No he ain't.

He is too. That's Hughie for you.

Is he drunk? What's the matter with you, son?

And Viv said, You know he cries when he makes love?

I was her lover and her best friend's husband and her Butlin's doctor and her hunger striker and shy stranger and Brendan Behan and ghost and sad bull and pimp and virgin cowboy and Dave Allen on his stool and her child and a magic talking-tree man and the invisible man and pagan chieftain and three window-cleaner brothers one stormy afternoon but she never let me be her bitch. It was the same night after the restaurant, a new request this, I asked her to use our one deep-frozen glass dildo on me and out she jumps from the bed like I was trying to oppress her. A week went by and she still couldn't look at me. I'm not going to apologise for it, she said, I can't do it, I just can't. I like my man to be a man. That's very deep, I said. Yes it is, profound actually, and you'll have to lump it. Shall I tell you a story about this man of yours you don't want to hear? Please don't then, Hugh. It's time, I said. The time is right. Your man was just out of his teens, living in London in a squat, not long over from Ireland. I know all this, she said. And all about how one day this terrible bitch upped and left poor Hughie, deserted him, and lo and behold he ended up sleeping on the streets. I know your adventures on the streets till I could act in them. Yeah well here's a new role, I said. One night I met this man in Victoria station, a man in a suit, with a leather briefcase and he asked me if I was hungry. He had missed his train, he said, and had time to fill. He had a faint Yorkshire accent. He offered to buy me some food in a café at the corner, on Vauxhall Bridge Road. An Italian place. You bet, I said. He asked me a lot of questions and god knows what I said because I was too busy stuffing my face on the food, bread and ham and then meatballs, I'd never had meatballs before. And then he said he was tired and had a hotel room nearby if I wanted to sleep on a proper bed, a real bed. Sheets. The smoothness. A soft mattress. A pillow. Yes please, I said. Did you really, Hughie? Yes I literally begged him. He laughed too. And I begged some more. Stop there, that's fine, she said. I don't need to hear the rest. Yes you do. You see Genevieve I was a young girl in his arms. And he petted me. And stroked me. And he was gentle. And he stopped when I told him to stop. And he kissed me on the back of the head and turned away from me and left me to enjoy the comfort and warmth which were even better than I imagined. Bliss. I fell asleep in bliss. A cheap hotel in Victoria? They probably weren't even fresh, she said. And I fell asleep, I said, and when I woke there was an animal on my back. I couldn't see him because I was pinned down. The power and the voice had to be a monster's. A demon. It was growling and gargling words, the violent stuff about how I had to be given to the beast. That happened to your man Genevieve.

So the dame missed her chance on that front. The subject was never broached again and the freezer door stayed shut. The Irish question took over her thoughts soon enough. The first airing was after a strange incident in the grounds of Alexander Palace. We were out for a walk on a decent evening like many another law-abiding couple, enjoying the open space and the glimpses of the yellow palace through the old trees which had found the energy to bud again. A black woman came running awkwardly across the grass toward us and stopped to ask us if we had seen her daughter. The woman was obviously at her wit's end. I tried to calm her, asked what the girl looked like, the stuff you're supposed to do. During this, Viv was shaking her head at me as if I shouldn't get involved. Then she pulled me aside and told me to stop encouraging the woman. She grabbed my phone. By the time I got it back, the woman had run off again.

We were arguing about it at home later. Viv saying she knew straight away the woman was a crazy and there was no missing child. I thought Viv was being cruel. Cruel? she said and happened to knock her glass off the table. It smashed. Viv didn't move. Are you waiting for me to? I said. No answer. I got the brush and pan from under the sink, swept it away, wiped the floor. Viv still hadn't moved.

That's never happened to me before, she said. Some new tone in her voice made me study her face. She was scared.

What? Breaking a glass? No big deal Viv.

She shook her head, unconvinced.

I take back the word cruel okay, I said.

It's not like me, she said.

What isn't like you?

She went to the bedroom. Hours later, I go to check on her, sit on the edge of the bed, and that's when she says it, Do you ever think about going home?

Travel was always the answer for that one. Way back when, it had been Latin America, then Berlin, Eastern Europe. And now Dublin. The grass was always greener on San Lazaro or Prenzlauer Allee or the Clontarf Road. I began to curse the airplanes sallying hither and thither about in the London skies. The cops stopped one night when I was pissing against the window of the local travel agents. Sure didn't I burn her lousy passport right in front of her. When she slipped out of the tapas bar on Green Lanes, noticed by only glossy Bollywood Sally and me, that's about where I had got to in the story, the passport burning.

Phase two this was, the Huddleston Road flat in Tufnell Park. Stucco ceilings, picture rails, an Edwardian hunting frieze around the living room. A massive wrought iron bed we didn't have sheets broad enough to fit.

You stole my passport you control freak?

Yes. I admit it. I damn well stole your passport. And I hid it in my porn stash.

We're around May Day here, 2001. Another protest rally planned. Reclaim the shagging streets. Smash the G8. I hadn't turned Tory or anything but the idea of being trapped in a big crowd had me waking up at night in a sweat. Viv said she understood but I knew deep down she was disappointed in me. I fucked her in a corner of the bed and harder again behind the front door before she left and then I stayed home and watched on the news how the cops corralled thousands of people for hours and the shit kicked off. Two full days later she arrives home. The only thing that kept me sane was that I had her passport.

The attack of the gay mutant stuff or the plain old bukake cheerleader?

There's this new stuff from India, really sick stuff with singing and dancing.

You wouldn't dare. Give it to me.

Watch me.

Why Hugh? Because I don't have a panic attack at the mention of a plane or a boat? Because I think there might be more to life than London? Don't I talk about us travelling together? Doing something else than the 9 to 5?

I like having a job. It's what us ordinary folk do. We go out the door and come back in the door. But you? That front door closes and I'm left wondering if you're ever going to darken it again.

Give it to me now. Right now.

Crap. It won't fucken catch. Who decided to make passports non-flammable?

Where are you going? We have to sort this out once and for all.

To find some fucking petrol.

She didn't stick around for long after. Five months we shifted our way through in Tufnell Park, the jungle wings of summer sunsets at her back as she straddled me on that sinister bed. Her purple hardside suitcase growing a pearl on top of the maple armoire. She had some job teaching English to foreign academics but she was bored. Behind the new long veil of fine red hair, she sat on the very edge of the antique chairs, reading books on the Crusades, smoking, hooked on the cheapest gin from the high street. It was eleven years since I'd seen her. How dare a dope like me even dream of making her tarry?

Stop staring at me, Hugh. I'm not going anywhere.

I wasn't thinking that. I was remembering one night in a certain gay bar.

Baloney. No you weren't.

Is your nose different?

People should stay in their homes, lock the doors and chain themselves to the bed. If they have to venture out they should cover their faces and speak to nobody. Infinite is the variety of what could happen to you al fresco. A decent day's work done, you've had a few pints and instead of going straight home you might fancy a kebab from your favourite spit in Camden. The pavement is a sad old rainbow and ends suddenly with you riding a tiger-skinned stool in a bar mirror, a high stage of multi-limbed heresies on behind you. This geezer next to you, white vest and a muscle throbbing in his waxed skull, could shout in your ear, There's no more fun to be had in London, which might tempt you to shout back, I wouldn't know mate, I'm a tourist myself over from Ireland. And you might buy him a drink and play the star-struck yokel but your new friend turns suspicious, thinks you're fibbing about being a paddy and waves another guy over, the small dapper type, who has personal experience of the emerald isle due to his auntie or sister in ancient Clonmacnoise, and these two might decide for reasons mystifying and probably perverse to expose the truth about you and your ethnicity, and the questions become sharp and spiteful and the dancers get stuck tighter together on the stage, until, perhaps, the dapper one has an idea and vanishes and returns unwrinkled with a girl in tow, a small busty chick with damp red hair, and this chick might stare at you in disbelief and you at her, and she could wink at you and say, I know how, and pull you off your stool and stick her hand between your legs under your ball bags. Oh this one's an Irish to be sure, a thoroughbred northerner if I'm not mistaken. Oh infinite are the ways.

Didn't this whole damn yarn of ours begin with a wink from her? Isn't that where I always start the story she despised me telling people? A squat in Stamford Hill. The nightly gathering of the time-travelling rabble in the upstairs room with the bits of stained glass in the bay windows. Cider and hash rollies and guitars. Winter 1990. Thatcher and the Poll tax. Troops Out. Black Flag. Spot a new face on the floor in the corner, a small thing, short red hair with a fringe, a walkman, oxblood DM's. Even with her knees up inside a baggy jumper you could still see the weight of the tits on her. A dent in her nose. And then she bloody winks at you. I thought there was something wrong with her.

Next morning in the kitchen, she's there at the table poking through a book. There's always people passing through the house so she could be somebody's sister, somebody's girlfriend. I nick a few slices of bread, stick them under the grill. Out the window, the long February streets run down to the canal and the marshes. Fumes of mixed fats fog the glass as Morrissey gripes in her walkman,

England is mine and it owes me a living. Her very first words to me while I'm scraping out a margarine tub, You have an arse like a girl's.

Now I was only a runt and easily pained. I hadn't much of a sense of humour then either. So I showed her what's what by pretending she didn't exist. Which worked fine until one Sunday morning arriving back from another squat somewhere, there she was sitting on the front stoop, shivering in her big jumper. I'm sorry, she said, I like your arse, I do, I just can't stand the noise of toast being buttered. Don't sit around the fucken kitchen then, I told her. Why are the IRA bombing Leicester? she said. How the fuck should I know? But you're from the north, she said. And you're not, I said. But I heard you were in a concentration camp, she said. I lost the rag, informed her it wasn't a fucken concentration camp, it was a big open camp you went to over the border if you had to leave your home in a hurry. The Free State Red Cross ran it. So watch out with questions or you might get your hooter broke again.

Years later, Genevieve would laugh it all away like it never happened. The politics, the arrests, the pub-collections, the dole offices, she was happy enough to hear me reminisce about but not the astonishment of her breasts in my hands or her clit-bean between my teeth the first time or her eyes when she was ready to let rip or my two fingers up her ass or what she could do with a condom or the bruises from her little heels pounding the back of this nervous young militant. And not the way, neither, how she deserted me after six and a half weeks.

I can date it exactly. The Poll tax riot, March 31st, 1990. I lost her in the crowd at Trafalgar Square when the cops ambushed us from behind on their silky steeds, a cavalry charge from an old history book, batons instead of swords. Blood leapt like flames from skulls around me. The roar that went up from the crowd, they must have heard it in Birmingham. A girl dropped at my feet, caught by a Metropolitan hoof. We had nowhere to run. People on their knees howling. Then the snatch squads in the black overalls. Blue helmets. I managed to climb some scaffolding, searching for Genevieve below. All creeds and colours dragged away by the ankles. And when the first shock had passed and the fight back began, I threw myself in. We smashed through the windows up to Leicester Square, gutting everything in our path. I was covered in blood now. A transit van clipped me and I got right back up again. Two bobbies nailed a black guy next to me. Another two dragging this New Ager woman by the arms and one of them won't forget me. Sometimes I stopped, just stood there and took in the chaos, staggered but admiring it somehow, the pigeons flying around in it. Then the blunt digit of a baton in the ribs. Up again and two grabbed me. And another two. They ripped the clothes off me in the struggle to get me into the back of the van. The bastards threw me naked into a cell.

You're doing what? Tobias said.

I'm moving to Dublin with Genevieve.

You're mouth is saying the words, son, but I don't see it.

We're moving to Dublin.

Keep trying.

After the cops charged me and let me out in charity-shop clothes, I went back to the squat. The Redzer and her rucksack were long gone. I wandered the streets for a few weeks. A man called Tobias, a bailiff, found me when he was clearing out a squat in Stamford Hill. A youngster in the basement, bricked up in a room, filthy, bonkers, who wouldn't even give his name.

You throw everything away for a whiff of the blarney cunt.

Go easy Tobias.

What have I taught you? Most men amount to nothing more than a—

I know. Fear begets truth. But this is what I want.

Wake up sunshine.

Being the gentleman he is, Tobias was big enough to offer to move our belongings across the water in a private container at his own expense. I remember what was supposed to be our last game of snooker together, and how, on a break of 82, he was speculating whether I might be useful to him in Dublin. I told him it was all off. Genevieve was gone again. For good this time. He was under the lamp, stretched for the white in the centre of the table. You're telling me you're staying now, he said. I nodded, shrugged or something. He destroyed the pink and came down the table in the shadows towards me. Stood in close, resting his weight on the cue between us. His smell of egg and rubber. The watery eyes tried to make mortal sense of me. You know something? he said. I bloody well hate snooker, always have, and he laughed so hard he had to sit down.

Long and shiny as the years, the tram slides by me now on Capel Street with The Redzer on its back. Now do I give chase? Infinite are the ways and means. In the barber shop up the street, the same one I used the day before I took the ferry to London, this tall fella on the scissors with a ponytail and a London accent. Archway his manor. Turns out there's a good chance he got on the same boat after I got off, going the other way to find his Irish roots. We took each other's place we decided. Kept the equilibrium. The kilter. And is it my other duty now to clatter through Dublin in pursuit of one sedentary Genevieve Querney with the light limbs and the sailor's wink. Blimey, there's my phone.

Bjorn. Perfect timing.

How was the flight? The pill was a help, yes?

Not a bother, Bjorn. How do you always know when I need you?

I am missing you terrible already. I can hear the gulls. So romantic.

You know what Bjorn. I'm a survivor. I'm fucken alive. Alive alive oh Bjorn.

Show me later. Which time you home tonight?

The City

the city is creative   the city says human creativity is the ultimate economic resource
the city turns human creativity into dreams and dreams into reality and reality into money
reality is money   the city says so   the city wakes early and takes a run in hyde park
before catching a circle line train to embankment   the city takes prozac and watches
daytime tv   the city is permanently at war   do not leave your baggage unattended
the city ate the past   it chewed it up and spat it out in sound bites and tourist trails and
marble museums   the city reinvented history and called it a show   the city ate the
future too   and spat out nothing   the city says be present in the present   set
your alarm clock and check your apps and iron your shirts for the week ahead   the city
speaks of revanchism in its architecture and multiculturalism in its billboards   the city
offers choice   and temporal euphoria   the city is deeply erotic   you love its
black tunnels and tall silver towers   you only pretend to dislike the smell of its bowels
the city expresses itself in a language that is sexual   mind the gap   the city offers
satiation before you experience desire   the city orders prawn tempura sitting in a cafe
on the bank of the river   staring at the river releases endorphins   the city drinks a
glass of chilled chardonnay   the city has a death-wish and an appetency for life style
the city is open for business   the city favours a late capitalist neo-liberal market
the city is not for sale   the city says everything is for sale   the city has already been
sold   the city thrives on tension   east and west   rich and poor   the city
dislikes mediocrity   mediocrity is death   the city sleeps at its desk after lunch but
perks up for a sales meeting in the late afternoon   the city believes in religion but not
in an afterlife   the city is tolerant   when it is hot the city riots and occasionally
beats people to death   the city loves peace   the city holds huge rallies where
everyone chants peace in technicolour newsreel   the city is a film shot in black-and-
white   on sunday mornings in kensington park trees drape their shadows over grass
while squirrels dash back and forth like commuters   at times like this the city loves you
back   the park is full of grey squirrels   all the red squirrels are dead   the city
smells of piss and broken promises   the city says sorry for your inconvenience when
people commit suicide   the city exists in one corner shop   on summer mornings the
city is covered in golden footprints that can only be seen from cranes   in winter the city
floats along milky white not caring where it is going   sometimes the city dies of
boredom   other times it paints itself red   after work the city drinks a pint of bitter in
a pub owned by a conglomerate   the city has colleagues not friends   the city takes
the bus home to ealing and eats fish 'n' chips from a bag   at night the city sheds dust and
colour   and swells   a collective unconscious where millions of dreams swim
through the darkness

Cathy Sweeney

Terror and Wonder: London Chronicle
Danny Denton

POST NO BILLS

Unreal City. Engine sounds. Mechanical breath. Beeping doors: mechanical voice. Yellow light, bright. A man slumped beneath a heavy coat, wearing small round glasses, his head iceberging the folds of an upheld newspaper. But he is sleeping, not reading. In the windows of the carriage there are shadowy reflections, illuminated ghosts of the passengers at a slanted angle. The city worker watches his reflection in the dark perspex: is he the ghost or the passenger?

Now and then, low voices. A cough. A sneeze. His phone falls from his hands to the carriage floor. The two-tone knock mirrors the train's wheel on a rail. It is a journey of staggering boredom, time melting into engine sound and into the small, rattling phone screen. The paling keen of the train through tunnels. Time is nervous: as long as the train sound is there, seconds and minutes are its prisoners, and they pass in their own lurching moments. It is seven o clock. Without warning, it is quarter past seven. And yet it seems like the city worker has only just now stirred to pick up his phone from the shuddering floor. The ghosts in the perspex continue to wait.

Unreal City.

At a certain point then the window's darkness is transformed into a moving picture of dim back yards, a labyrinth of awnings and tarpaulins heavy with water. And the high rises then too, and dark shimmering yellow streets and murky canals. Roundabouts, car parks, estates, Sainsbury's Locals… Like foreign languages partly known, he can almost understand their rhythms. Streetlights and rooftops spread out into the distance; as the city spreads out into this massive sprawl he loses his grip on meaning. This view, this window, has become a kind of visual rambling, a scrapheap of ideas and images. The city is the mind of a mad raving lunatic, a relentless sob. Unreal City.

He slips off the train into the belly of the station and paces the platform towards the barriers. It is like a race for air. Beep beep. Unreal City. The breath now of traffic, and the punctuation of traffic lights, sounds of horns and motors and the hiss of roadwater swept along. He hears from the radio of a news vendor on the street that a lorry has overturned on the A2 at Blackheath, spilling tons upon tons of gravel over the road.

BUT WHO IS THAT ON THE OTHER SIDE OF YOU?

Dusk opens the chasm of night and the darkness grows from grassy ground shadows. Car and lorry lights bleed in squinted vision, in a long bright river of light that cuts through the dimming expanses of heath. Sounds of horns and motors. Roads are referred to as arteries, like some vast body exists. I think of them as rivers glistening. Darkening church steeple rises into vast turquoise, the sky scarred by planes, their whale song playing off the breath of traffic on the hill, approaching the roundabout. In the van on the way to training, Mick Rogers has been singing along to Big Tom, but pauses to tell me that, in the Seventies, he used to come here to help the circus workers take the Big Top down. They'd be in a rush to move on to the next place and so they'd pay men cash to fall in and help. An idea for a speech comes to me, about belonging, about the lack of a parish but the presence of something else. About *transcience*. But Big Tom is filling the air again, and Mick is swearing at a cyclist who has cut along the inside. The windows are steaming up something savage; I am forever thinking of dressing-room speeches that will never be given. I perambulate the city, composing sentences to be delivered to stuffy, crowded dressing rooms.

'How many do you think will be up tonight?' Mick asks. To the cyclist: 'Will you ever fuck off out of my way?'

WHAT IS THE ESSENTIAL ROOT? CONSTANT DOCUMENTATION

Ian Guthrie thinks of *Frankenstein*, as he slowly edges onto the roundabout, no longer fears the wide lean of the London bus as it comes round too fast. He has heard that Justin Lake—his own personal hero in the teaching game—finally lost his head in just such traffic. That he waited too long for a red light to change and, pulling an umbrella from the passenger seat, got out to smash up his own front windscreen. Guthrie remembers stopping a fight in the classroom once, two Year 9s. When he put his forearm out to hold one boy back, he felt the fourteen-year-old heart pounding so fast beneath the white shirt.

A space is cleared in the wake of the bus and Guthrie nips into it, jeered then by a chorus of beeping. He is tired; the night will pass like a yawn. He curses the cyclist, who thrusts out a luminous yellow arm and veers in front of him.

Guthrie stirred his coffee once, continually, for thirty-five minutes. He does not remember what he thought about.

OVERHEARD IN LONDON

Two minks snarl at each other over the bottle universe of a model ship. Paint peels from the bulb-bathed walls.

'I admit that I am sometimes hypnotised by the patterns of the Tube upholstery. Whole minutes pass…'

'You are not invited into homes here.'

'No: you only get to meet people in cafés… restaurants… pubs. The *public domain*. It's so… impersonal.'

'I miss the kitchens of others.'

'Aye, but it's the people that make it.'

'Ahyeah: it is of course. Another of those warm, wet things?'

'Absolutely.'

Jug Jug Jug.

'The drivers here are fucking terrible.'

'They **are**: they indicate as they turn, not before.'

'I left home in search of my 'bush' soul.'

'Look what you found.'

'Cafés in churches.'

'…'

'Have I become such a negative person?'

'You are tired and bored.'

'Do you hear the sirens? Even now they burst in upon me!'

CULLING IS A CON!

In a Wetherspoon's pub, the woman of middle age has ordered a bowl of chips to go with her pint of Shipyards. In her seat beneath a roadside window, she leans forward, her black trouser suit and white blouse hanging loose, like old skin, her black leather handbag placed neatly on the table in front of her. She could have come from work in a bookies, or a city office. Her hair is unbrushed, wind-wild; she places her hands palmdown on her thighs, crosses her ankles beneath the creaky wooden chair. Table 25 is a dark wooden plane of spilled salt and dried ketchup.

Mostly, she hears without interest the matter-of-fact confidences of men, in twos, estimating and counting and dividing the quantities of things. The thirst for knowledge has left an overabundance of… everything. Unshaven, they tally their change. Jug Jug Jug. Twit Twit Twit. No music plays over them, so that the conversations must combine to make their own jilted rhythms, supported only by the sporadic bleepfall music of a till, or a fruit machine. Her eye passes over the corduroyed men, and over the hungover students, who pull at their clothes and their haircuts, or tuck their hands between pursed thighs, and she settles eventually for the rolling subtitled news footage of a satellite channel, playing high up in the corner of the pub wall. The HGV lorry has been responsible for the deaths of nine London cyclists already this year. She imagines their ghosts cruising the city at night, forever bound to London's myriad itineraries, London's labyrinthine maps, wheels spinning with eternal purpose, ghost-legs tirelessly pumping, working the brakes, leaning into pock-marked street corners…

When a bowl of oildamp, steam-giving, thick-cut chips arrives and an eastern accent offers *yourerder* she slowly and carefully draws from her black leather purse a large jar of Hellman's mayonnaise, three-quarters full, her wrists and ringless fingers firmly poised, already forming the practised grip. The window above her faintly rattles. Her mind allows a half-formed thought to pass.

STAND BACK TRAIN APPROACHING

Derek and Kathy walk down the steps at London Bridge onto the marble-tiled promenade, and with cold wind cutting across their chests they hop the thick black chain and descend seaweed-polished steps to the brownstreaked shore of the Thames. The barges lie low on cold, concrete water, as the wind carries dirty breakers in toward the two walking.

'He never lets me alone,' Derek says as he feels out for her hand.

'Talk to him.'

'Always at my fucking shoulder… He's a control freak.'

Across the water, innumerous office lights blink on and off in the square-mirrored palaces of the shoreline. On-the-clock cleaners are held within the tiny lights, bent over, traversing cable-strewn carpet tiles in sweeping arcs. As it darkens, these lights begin to draw their nightly path across the water, meeting the two shadows that reach for the water.

'My back hurts. I can't even sneeze.'

The swells of the Clipper racing west usher in rushed sighs and Derek's frustration is captured. The squat barges give the illusion of drift.

The giddiness of foreign languages passes above the couple, on the promenade, faces and bodies neither of them can see. His eye falling closer to the shoreline, where Kathy is making statements about the cranes on the horizon, Derek spots it first.

'Look,' he says, breaking away to point at something washed nearly all the way up to the wall, on its side and stiff against the nudge of his suede ankle boot. Pink, like a latex-covered car part, it glows up at them from the sand.

'A dildo,' he exclaims.

'A Rampant Rabbit,' she corrects.

'I bet,' says Derek, 'that some girl cast it out after she finally got engaged.'

'Or some jealous bloke chucked it out over the balcony when he found it in the bottom on the knicker drawer.'

Derek looks at her suddenly. 'Have you got one?'

She laughs. Behind their backs, the Thames licks its way towards them, sweating oil and tar and dreary silt. Above, the ivy-dressed balconies of the wharf's boutique riverside apartments loom, as if trying to test their value with the leaden river, asking, *Who is the fairest of them all?*

Cool wind ruffles the backs of the couple as they prospect further about the pink object. The sturdier heft of the buses on London Bridge rises over the shush of the breaking waves. Only when Derek and Kathy have sufficiently told the possible varied histories of the Rampant Rabbit do they feel able to leave it there, to be collected again by the river and swallowed up, and already then they are rehearsing beneath the realms of their eveningtalk how they will play this one out in the Marquis on Friday night, before the long-practised and expectant grins of the other couples they know.

WHAT SHALL I DO NOW? WHAT SHALL WE DO TOMORROW?

The single span arch roof of St. Pancras Station contains the leaden grey sky. From the bleachcleaned platforms below, the tired shifting of trains drifts up into the vast iron and glass vault of it, that sound mingling with the footfall of passengers and the distant strains of a hidden quartet. Sterile announcements punctuate Rachel's thoughts as a group of teenagers with yellow backpacks rush for the Eurostar.

There will be Bolivian rugs again, and incense smells, and no longer the sticky laminate floors, or the random discovery of cigarette butts or bottle caps. Her mother used to bring her cups of tea in bed. Will she do so again? During my studies I have grown as a person. I am available immediately. Behind the freestanding glass elevator a dreadlocked man pulls faded trousers up at the thighs and sits to play the piano. His overture lifts past the iron framework, past the gridwork cables and exposed vents, to join the ghostly confusion of the grandiose vault arch. *Last exam today! Won't know what to do with myself!* All these words and sounds will be ghosts one day, floating in the ether like dust, with nowhere to go, and the buildings will dream of us, the memory of us.

Rachel walks along the concourse of shops, all behind plate glass. Others stroll, others hurry, from concrete baluster to concrete baluster, as she looks for presents to buy for the family. A Paddington Bear? Books? It has not been very long since she saw them last, but this feels significant.

This was all a beer cellar once—she knows from coursework—but now as she passes under the redbrick arches of the undercroft, the floor spotlights creating spooky triangular shadows, it is an arcade that signifies the city: Costa; WHSmith; Eat; Boots; M&S; and so on towards Calgary or Purgatory. Perhaps that is it: each of them here, each of the throng has died in this city, and St. Pancras is the halfway house. Down here, on the concourse with the shopping pigeons, on the platforms, you are waiting to have your details processed and your ticket number called. And up there, through the huge iron ribs and glass arch of the great greenhouse, is the grey leaden face of God. The Chrome Unknown. *So scary to be finished in Uni. Go easy on me world!* She counts the flattened chewing gum in pale mosaic tiles. She has always been early for trains.

WHAT BRANCHES GROW OUT OF THIS STONY RUBBISH?

One. One. Three. One. Three…

Zero…

You are third in the queue…

You are second in the queue…

You are first in the queue…

Hello, I'd like to set up a direct debit to pay my credit card bill each month.

Hello—welcome to Barclay's Telephone Banking. Can I take your name, please?

Yes, my name is Danny Denton. I'd like to set up a direct debit.

Hello, Mr Denton. How can I help you today?

Yes, I'd like to set up a direct debit.

Sorry, the cafe is closing in fifteen minutes, sir, and the toilet is now closed for cleaning.

But you are the only member of staff here, and you're cleaning the coffee machine, not the toilet. Can't I just use the toilet quickly?

Mr Denton, before I can help you, I need to ask you some security questions. Can you confirm your postcode?

SE4 2LG.

Thank you. Can you confirm your date of birth?

Fifth of the Fourth, Eighty-Three.

Thank you. Can you confirm the third digit of your passcode?

…

Mr Denton?

Hang on a second. You're telling me that even though the toilet is empty, and you're not cleaning it, it is still closed for cleaning?

Yes, I've dropped my phone and the screen has smashed, and I need to claim on my insurance policy, and I've been told that I need to order the forms from you.

Yes, sir. As I've explained, the toilet closes at quarter to five, PM.

Even though I've been here all day, drinking coffee you served me and that I paid for?

So I need to order the form from you, and I can't do it online. And then I fill the form out and send it to you. Then you send me another form if you think I have a valid claim, and I complete that form, and send you the phone with that form, and then you decide if my claim is successful?

Three.

Thank you, Mr Denton. One last question…

Can I use the toilet if I promise to be back out before you have even finished cleaning the coffee machine, and if I also promise to make zero mess?

What is your mother's maiden name?

How long would I be without my phone?

Can I just use the fucking toilet please!

I am afraid I cannot confirm that, Mr Denton, as we would need all forms completed and also have to carry out a technical investigation. We do endeavour to return all items as soon as possible.

Your aggression is not appreciated or warranted, sir.

Phelan.

Thank you, Mr Denton. What can I do for you today?

I'd like to set up a direct debit, to pay my credit card bill.

Okay Mr Denton, I am going to put you on hold so that I can transfer you to the correct department for setting up a direct debit.

Can you see the madness in the fact that I've been sitting here, under that window over there, all day, drinking coffee that you served me and which I paid for. Now that I need to urinate that coffee out of my system, you will not allow me to, even though you have a perfectly functioning and unoccupied toilet beyond that partition wall?

[*hold music*]

Drip. Drop. Drop. Drop. Drip. Drip.

THIS AREA IS MONITORED BY 24-HOUR CCTV SURVEILLENCE

Endless rows of terraced houses with bay windows, protected by four-foot brick walls. The roots of cherry blossoms crack the pavements so that they roll like waves, blistering the tarmacadam that has filled whole purgatorial A&E wards with sprained ankles, on late fluorescent nights at Lewisham Hospital, with injured offenders handcuffed to benches, their wrists twisted as they try to sleep off the drink and police officers swipe their phones with fatigued fingers. Residents leave out the things they don't want anymore: flimsy wardrobes, crumpled shoes, dusty video cassette collections. Elastic bands and other litter are strewn all over the pavement. The smell of marijuana eases from a cracked open yet curtainguarded window, or perhaps the adjacent cobbled alleyway. The city worker limps by, away home with his sausages and eggs in a blue plastic bag, the *Daily Mail* tucked into a damp armpit. On the other side of the road, screened by parked cars, a wheelie suitcase gathers momentum. Every thirty or so seconds another planes soars overhead, filling the sky with its scraping song. A straight-backed cyclist cruises by the city worker, whistling, avoiding the speed bumps. When he crests the hill, panting slightly, he will take in with awe the view of the city buildings, vague, lightless, dim glassy, clustered too close together beyond the blue haze of the bright morning's smog. A siren suddenly comes wailing down the street, materialising from nowhere and, as always, disappearing to nowhere again, the call of the banshees his father feared once cancer came.

His flat is dim, always, with the huge acanthus outside the window blocking the spring light that comes in low over the terraced houses. Under the window, a clothes horse dank with wet trousers and shirts. On the corner television he half-watches a show about a Scarborough steeplejack felling industrial chimney stacks, the screen filled with smoke and side streets and market places and city rooftops. But the city worker's eye is drawn then to the window, as snow begins to drift across beyond the venetian framed panes, flecking the acanthus all with white. Then he realises it is not snow, but the drifting flowers of the street's cherry blossoms.

MIND THE GAP

'Say it. *Lo-wer Glan-mire Road*. It's like a song.'
'*Low-er Glan-mire Road*. It is!'

IF THERE WERE ONLY WATER

It makes a sound, the city. Granted we were stoned but from the top of the reservoir, looking out over the orange haze of a hundred thousand buildings, you could hear that sound. A kind of stirring, a festering, inhaling and exhaling at the same time. Hear now the whale song of aeroplanes, beeps, vibrations, the steady murmur of pubs, restaurants, the electric whir of sockets and appliances, the steady, ever-breaking wave of air-conditioning, a million overheard conversations, the intoning of engines and vents: an eternal drone... Up on the reservoir, all these voices came to us, and they were part of the machine, and the machine was traffic heard from a distance, an old coach engine on the road at night, when you are half-asleep and the way is straight and the speed is fixed, a tumble dryer rolling incessantly in another room...

FURNISHED TWO-BED FLAT TO LET

'Got banned from driving after an in-cee-dent in Oz. Wrapped her round a pole and woke up in a bush.'

'Fucking hell.'

'Bean garda came. Took me to the station. Took the license off me and I never got it back.'

Hands are swollen. He challenged someone to an arm wrestle not ten minutes ago, a big Russian-looking buck in a tight T-shirt. I cannot bring myself to trust a man who does not take his coat off in a pub. We've been drinking since we got on the tube at South Ruislip, but he materialised somewhere between Greenwich and New Cross.

'Why weren't you at the game today?'

'Work.'

'Oh. Where were you at it?'

'Stansted there. Clocked off early. Big staff party for finishing the stage. Nine pints I had before we left the site.'

'And how did you get from Stansted to here? Airport bus?'

'Drove.'

'Nine pints and you drove? Sweeney, you fucking lunatic! Are you insane?'

'Woh. Woh. Hang on. Cool your jets. Why is it that people think a man can't drive when he's drunk? If I have the capability to drive when I'm sober, do I suddenly forget how when I'm drunk? Do I forget how to talk when I'm drunk? Do I forget how to walk when I'm drunk?'

'No. Of course not.'

'Well then.'

'But your capacity for doing so is massively hindered. You stagger, you don't walk. You slur. Your driving goes to shit... Think, man! What if you killed a young family driving back from Stansted this night?'

'Maybe I did.'

'Maybe you... What?'

'Come on now. How would I do that?'

'...'

Leans in close, confides: 'Listen to me. Listen to this. A fella on the site told me today that on the council estate where he lives, out beyond Stokey that is, that there's this woman there who was pregnant for ages.'

'Ages?'

'Well, for nine months I suppose. As you do. But when her time came she gave birth, not to a baby, but to three little white rabbits. Rabbits!'

Looks earnestly. Believes.

'Rabbits, listen. She was Chinese, he said. Do you think something like that could be the truth?'

LOSS IN TRANSIT IS A PART OF LIFE

Realising that his feet could not touch the ground in Ireland, and with the wave that carried him from Tír na nóg broken, Óisín had little choice but to ride his horse to Rosslare and take the ferry, like so many Irish women and men before him, to England.

Safe to disembark as he was at sea again, he left his tireless white steed Embarr in the steel-echo car hold, alongside Avensises, Volkwagens, Scania trucks, caravans and Harleys, where, when her water was gone, she lapped an enormous fleshy tongue against a small pool of leaked engine oil. She began then to shudder with the engines and the dark waves beyond the painted hull.

Three floors up, Óisín paid silver and paper for a pint of porter and a plate of pie and potatoes, and stalked across a cafe of motionless bodies. It was gloomy. He settled on an upholstered bench beneath a window with blackened sea view, and rested his plate on his knees. Guttural snores held themselves against the steady motors of the vessel, smell of socks and soft farts and jeans never washed. Some strange spell, he decided, drawing from his pint and wiping foam from his lip. Sitting up straight he watched them sleepwalk to the toilets and back, turning then from side to side as they tried to settle back into sleep, waking again to configure playlists on smartphones, pulling their hoods over their eyes. Eventually, his youthful eye settled on the bottom of a girl, curled across two seats with her back to him and a sliver of pale blue knickers showing.

'Fair maiden,' he whispered, lifting one great buttock to release a silent fart himself, the gas of ages, the breath of eternal youth.

As dawn broke on the Irish Sea they began to stir. Óisín was brought back from his recollection of epics, as they began to gather their things quietly; they made their toilet alongside each other, splashing their faces with cold water and rubbing baby wipes into their armpits. Instead of *travellers*, the disembodied announcements referred to *passengers*. Many journeyed without passports, or with pets, or with criminal records in the print of their worn thumbs. They were armed with smartphones and backpacks, or great chests of suitcases that went only reluctantly. These people carried their whole lives with them, Óisín realised, struggling with the zips of the heavy bags that would contain them.

At the bar, the only men who would drink with Óisín told him that the Irish had fucking built the place; that the place was three-quarters Irish for all the Irish blood, bone, sweat, tear, straining muscle and broken heart that went into the building of that country and the being away from home sweet home.

'Tis our song it sings beneath the sirens,' one of them mourned, gulping.

'What about the other quarter?' Óisín asked. Without socks between his feet and his brogues, and with a woolly jumper and a floppy blond fringe, he looked like any other of the emigrating hipsters travelling to the land of hipsters.

'A mixture,' came the answer. 'None of it clean.'

When Óisín returned to his faithful steed Embarr he found that she had transformed into a dirty white HiAce with a rusty undercarriage, two thirds of a tank of diesel, and a back which contained a single mattress and a few second-hand tools. Some smartarse with a vandalising finger had written the words 'CLEAN ME' into the grime of the back sliding door. Sighing, Óisín climbed into the HiAce and started her on the third go.

The journey passed in ancient song, but as he approached distant London, the youthful warrior was confused by a great bland data smog. Everything was vague, vaguer than ever before.

It was at Watford Gap he stopped first, on the M1, bursting for the toilet. But the moment his feet touched the ground, didn't three-quarters of him suddenly age three thousand and a bit years, and disintegrate in the forecourt of the garage. The quarter that remained included a thick, muscle-strangled left arm, the neck and left sleeve of a Fruit of the Loom T-shirt, and a blond young head that didn't look too surprised, that would have been easily mistaken for any one of the trendy young hipster faces swanning around Shoreditch at that time. The same blond hair was ruffled by the slipstream of the cars that zipped by on the forecourt, all in a hurry to fill up and move on, and when a part-time, zero-hour contract employee found the remains a half hour later, a Coronas song was still playing from the cabin stereo of the white HiAce.

SHE IS BORED AND TIRED

The local talks about bus routes like they are old myths and legends. 'The 54 used to go by the shopping centre in Bexleyheath once. Now it goes straight to the terminus…'

He worked in theatre once; now he awakens in bus depots in the furthest reaches of the night, his phone escaped him, his wallet open on the seat and empty of cash, his wife not even stirring in her slumber. No friendly Caribbean bus driver to put an arm around him or give him a hot cup of tea to set him off, only condensation on the dark baubled windows obscuring the lonely depot lights, the empty buses, and foxes frightened out of ground-licking when he hits the emergency door release and stumbles out into the cold, his stupid hand repeatedly going for a phone that isn't there and a wallet that cannot help him. It is approaching dawn. Twit twit twit.

FOLLOW US ON TWITTER

'In the city, words are threats.'

'Say something constructive.'

'The city remains intact.'

'The city is a great steaming mess of perspex and tar, an unfinished encyclopaedia of road signs, bricks, warnings and worn soles.'

'The city is breath… the breath of the bus driver out the window as he curses the cyclist… the breath of the cyclist pulling back… the breath of the fat, tumourous pigeon trying to take off… the breath of six secondary students dividing twelve-packs of doughnuts outside Poundland so that they can sell them on in school…'

'The city is lived, measured and experienced differently by eight million different souls, each processing their surroundings and composing a unique stream of consciousness. So, as such, it is eight million cities.'

'Fuck that! The city is a machine. This enormous, complex, intricate machine, all oil and tar and smoke and dirty water. Do you feel part of the machine? Do you recognise that all your efforts, all your entertainments, your digestions, are all just part of the machine's movement, as it burrows tick-like deeper and deeper into the earth? You have long ago abandoned yourself to its rhythms…'

'The city is not a machine! It is a process in time, a simple action, an accumulation of seconds and minutes. You know, first, before cities, there was agricultural time, when people measured their lives via the seasons. You slept more in winter, rose earlier in summer, with the sun. You rested when there wasn't work to be done. Then cities. Then industries. Then people working in shifts to a new kind of time. Industrial time. They start at nine, finish at six. London Bridge is falling down falling down falling down. Lives are suddenly clockwork patterns. A great crowd swells. There are rush hours; there is leisure time. TV comes along, inhales that leisure time. Weekends are discovered, like fossils that had always been there. Sport becomes regulated. The Internet. All of a sudden we're carrying the lives of others around in our pockets on little battery-powered devices. Every spare minute—whether you're on the toilet or in the queue for a sandwich at Pret—you are on your smartphone, being entertained, and every minute of the day you know what time it is. This city is that time, and you are just something that ticks inside it, along with all the other beeps and clicks and whirs.'

'Well, let me show you a place fable has not dreamt of, nor sun nor moon scattered. Who will follow me to the ends of red brick and grey brick? Who will read the legends of the graffiti to me? Let's trace our hands roughly on the bright colours, forged in the early hours by foxes in hoods…'

'… is the breath of two West Indian students dragging their feet to the DLR station… is the breath of the market trader calling, 'POUND-A-BOWL!'… is the breath of morning church shufflers finishing their cigarettes and making sure that when flung they land on the other side of the church wall… is the breath of five-a-side footballers on a freezing February night, under floodlights, on astroturf… is the breath of the homeless girl, the kebab shop worker, the five million weeknight drinkers of the greater metropolitan area, the trainline workers, strolling the tracks, their boots grinding the hardcore, making a harder sound than snow, as the late night turns over… is the breath of maybe ten million sleepers heaving out and up over train lines and rooftops to form a kind of supernatural glow, a glue that keeps that city intact, keeps it from collapsing into a trillion confused fragments…'

'Nobody in London's head is on straight; everybody's head tilts a certain way.'

'But there's this notion… that we pre-date the city, that we'll outlive it. You feel it, walking in the map, amongst it all, noting the ancient monuments and the historical streetnames. It's a kind of sense… But we won't outlive cities. Of course not. The city is an illusion of some eternal story.'

'I see crowds of people walking around in a ring.'

WHAT SHALL WE EVER DO?

'I can't help but notice you admiring the brickwork,' says a voice close by.

A soft face, grey hair combed. Blue EMR vest over puffed standard-issue EMR jacket. Armed with long-handled pan, short-handled brush.

'I did a project on the construction of St. Pancras last year.'

'Ah, then you're noting the arches built in all along there.'

Not knowing what to say, she smiles. I want to practise architecture in the city that is at the forefront… This city is a labyrinth of architectural wonders; I am inspired by each and every building that I walk past. I am reliable. I am trustworthy. I am creative. I am adaptable. In ten years I want to be running my own practise. I feel I can bring great energy to the role. I am available immediately…

He points through the roof. 'Witness the golgotha of cranes.'

She pulls out the right headphone. 'Sorry?'

'This is the world's only neo-gothic train shed,' he repeats.

'Ah. An inspiring workplace.'

'You said it. I'll never retire.' The elbow blow he gives her is softened by the padding of his jacket. 'Not that I can afford to anyway. This effing government, ay?'

He clears his nostrils into his throat and swallows. 'Worked here since I was fourteen.'

'Wow.'

'Remember when this beautiful glass roof was covered with bloody Welsh slate. On account of the bombs.'

'Wow.'

'I helped clear the rubble from platforms three and four when the bombs fell through that time.'

'Really?'

'Remember choking on the brick dust. The smell of it… And overturned carriages and splintered wood all round. Even the rats were scared that time.'

'I smell coffee and paper now… Why is there no graffiti here?'

'Takes a fleet of twelve men to prevent that sin… Where are you headed?'

'Sheffield.'

'Safe journey then.'

Forged from the minerals of the Erewash Valley, the station is a triumph of verticality and light. Please find attached my curriculum vitae in application for the post. The famous DENT clock-face with its gold leaf rim surveys the cacophony of wheelies and trains, the endless platform, the kissing of fifty-foot lovers. I am ready to take the next step in my career. Should you require anything further from me, please don't hesitate to get in touch.

When it is time to depart, she walks the long platform. In the vast vault of the station her worries no longer feel merited. There will be jobs. Breath fogs on the cold air. The rattle of wheelie cases mimics the rumble of trains on the cold steel tracks. Human life is like one of those Russian dolls. This is a place of echoes. I had not thought so many had died. The coffee stands and chocolate stands are left behind; there is the hiss of passenger doors. There is minding the gap, and mice scurrying below. Engines siphon, roll, warm. The chrome monolith advertisements are gone now too. Bags are pressed into shiny overhead shelves. Back the way she has come, a multitude of heads arching up towards departure boards. She feels the bombs coming. I am available immediately. Cranes peer in through the arch glass above all. What is all this commotion?

CYCLISTS BEWARE. THIS VEHICLE STOPS REGULARLY.

Sweeney's Hophead has a red heart, glowing, flickering. The wall's plaster swells in layers that look like magnolia bread slices; wall and ceiling are grotesque with this plaster finish, decades old. A cityscape of board game boxes hangs in the balance on a table in the corner, overseen by a stuffed peregrine falcon in a glass case, a model of a golden sailed Chinese schooner, and a tall vase of plastic green leaves. Sweeney has been paid and clocked out early. His time now is his own again to waste. The whole crew are on their way.

He never goes long without thinking of that Chinese woman, on the estate. His washed and cut fingernails test themselves on his forearms, leaving pale skindusty trails like planes on a clear sky. Light comes from the red candle glass on his glossy table, from a cast-iron, star-shaped light fixing, from the ship's lamps that hang every ten or so feet as far as the counter. Two giant, gold-plated, white-painted masquerade faces grin down at him from the mantelpiece. The coat hooks are faun hooves; the faun's head sticks out from above the mirror. The Montague is, famously, the last stop before Paris. The place was closed for a while, but it is back with a bang now.

'We're en route,' comes the Whatsapp response.

It is a city of endless routes, he has often said. Whole lives are lost in the planning of a tube journey. He told a girl: he told her, 'Fourteen African children have died of starvation in the time it took you to decide whether to take the Northern line or the Jubilee on your *odyssey* to Tottenham Court Road.' Afrobeat follows grunge follows a metal classic that Sweeney remembers from outside his brother's closed bedroom door, way back in time. A warped red glow runs across the tall brass containers against the wall beneath the window; Sweeney eveningdreams of churns, milk factories, pasteurisation. Jive music now, beats itself against exposed pipes and vents, and glossypolished wood panels. Someone behind the bar is calling over a bad line something like, 'I swear dead boatmen are haunting the docks.'

Where the fuck are they? On the 54? The 171? Old framed pictures depict garish landscapes dominated by uniformed generals with waxed moustaches, under autumn skies, shadowed by pale women with red lips. They point, or plant their hands on their hips. They fucked the Nazis right good alright, but didn't the Germans win in the end…

'Anyone for the Blythe,' comes the suggestion.

They're on the 53; they're rubbing the windows with their jacket sleeves right now, watching out for their stop. He can see them, in his mind's eye, noting the locations of bookies, taxi ranks and chicken shops. Ogling women. They say number 127 on that road is a sex cinema. You have to look for the Western Union sign. It is blackened by grime. These streets would choke you; he has often told them this. Where are they?

Goodnight, sweet ladies! Goodnight! That jive music has haunted him all the way from the Montague. He decided not to make for Dover or Paris, but is trickling back now through the crowded bus stops of the New Cross Road. The plaster of his mind peels. He wrote 'Fuk U' on the chalks board outside. Anthony might be in the Marquis. Or Mattie. He had to get out—it felt like those pancake bread walls were collapsing in on him. He nearly took the electric heater and the falcon with him but he was stopped at the door. Where are ye boys? Where are ye boys? His battery is dead. The weekend is almost over.

LITTER CAUSES DELAYS

The cyclist cruises down the brokenglasstarmac of the Ilderton Road, location of at least ten punctures over the few years he has cycled it, and is overtaken by streptococcal lorries. In the diminishing light the traffic lights pulse and he presses the brakes gently to bring him into the cyclist's zone. In the city you grow used to waiting. You die slowly and patiently. As the green man disappears a rasta begins to cross, pulling his tracksuit bottoms up around his belly as he shuffles on. On his tours the cyclist has freewheeled over broken glass, past vast mounds of rubble behind rusty fences, and hills of rubbish for sorting in container yards by men with high-viz vests and doctor's gloves. He has encountered whole monopolies of storage unit and warehouse, behind locked gate, facing onto murky canals, and fleets of shiny white vans parked uniformly in industrial yards. Each gate, each road and lane and warehouse contains a mystery, a secret history. From atop reservoirs he has surveyed the whole city, its myriad eyes blinking, and he has lost himself in the supernova of it.

The light beats orange and he eases a blackgloved hand out to the right. At green he is already gone, turning and dipping beneath the overpass. The chrome sky is blocked out a moment, and then he is passing along railway arches and down into Bermondsey and closer to the river and the city. His feet will not touch the ground again until Moorgate.

He avoids the chunks of broken concrete on the quieter back roads, and slows to take the savagery out of the speed bumps. Hooded figures haunt the estates. The cyclist is wary of clear plastic sheeting that has gotten caught on wasteland shrubs. Every built thing has the human mark of spray paint. That, he thinks, is how we can be sure we exist. This all started with a red powdery hand on a cave wall in France, ten thousand years ago.

KEEP RIGHT

Follow with your mind's eye the city worker—the passenger—skipping down the tile steps of the underground at St. Paul's. He leaves the great, snow-powdered dome behind him and hurries down one side of the staircase, his mac rippling around him, TfL posters warning him to tread carefully as he hurries, pacing to the barriers, slipping his Oyster card from his pocket gracefully, slipping in ahead of a woman who fumbles with her purse, striding with impatient confidence into the automated embrace of the ticket barrier, slapping his card down, inhaling the singular and positive green beep of it—driving across his synapses a Pavlovian thrill of muscle-remembered pleasure, of social acceptance—his body already knowing the split second it takes to register the green beep, during which he has slowed, then moved on, is gone, is a ghost in the silver polish of the walls, the post casings, as a straight-line trajectory in the dead colourless eye of the CCTV feed, the time marked as 17 34 07 and counting, ceaselessly counting amidst the disembodied informational voices of the ticket halls and tunnels, and the passenger—the city worker—already arriving at the top of the downward escalator, at the forefront of a competitive *pedoton* of other commuters, some rushing simply to stand still on the razor-blade steps of the escalator, but he is descending, with no time—NO TIME!—to wait, instead squeezing by those who cling to the right, whose kitbags and handbags are jutting out, saying to their backs, 'EXCUSE ME,' as they gaze into windows of advertisement, moving image… Be a Well Man… Be a Well Woman… Treat all staff with respect… but our passenger has ingested these particular realities so many times that they rattle around his head without him even looking for them, and he is already stepping neatly from the escalator step as it flattens, returns underground, one polished black shoe outstretched, onto the buffed tiles down there, away from all natural light, and he paces then through a series of tunnels, hurtling deeper and deeper into the polish and grime underworld of the Tube, where a great crowd swells.

YOU ARE NOW ENTERING ZONE ZERO

Emerging suddenly at Tower Bridge, from between office blocks and greenblueglassy hotels, the cyclist is taken aback by the thousands of palpitating smartphones of the tourists along the city bridges. He crosses at Tower Bridge as it impresses itself upon the evening, the westward sky paling blue to peach, sunglow falling and spreading and fading in a dome beyond city towers of dark glass. Streetlamps follow the riverside paths like fairy lights and the lights of city offices twinkle and twitch like the readings of some immense pulsating switchboard. Just Westward, the Shard is a dark tower, a lord overlooking all, its glowing tip a beacon to the nightland, or perhaps some alien code. Two bronzed bomber-jacketed teenagers are taking selfies, manoeuvring their bodies to take in the sights of the city. He remembers so little about his own teenage years; it is as if the terabytes of sensory and informational data and the hundreds of pints he has consumed in the city since his longpast arrival have overwritten them.

From Tower Bridge to Bishopsgate he takes the medieval lanes that curve through old stone buildings, emerging now and then into the glare of phallic, extraterrestrial towers. Staring forms lean out from doorways. At one point he sees a group of dishevelled men and women in long dark coats, gathered at the foot of a back entrance stairs, listening as they are spoken to by their leader, also in a long dark coat, orating from the landing on the first flight of the fire escape. He is saying something that sounds like, 'The city is…' The cyclist knows of all manner of secret societies in the city, and was once a member himself of the London Rubble Association.

The Gherkin looms; the Heron Tower looms; their dark glass is protean, depthless. He could see immediately that the other man carried more weight than his profile pictures let on. He was older too, though that wasn't necessarily a bad thing. But he was not his profile; he was another person. It felt important to note this. They staggered across the first few minutes of conversation, far-reaching vacuums of pubsound between each smileguarded sentence.

'How long have you been in London?'

'Four years.'

'Don't they say that if you make it five consecutive years you never want to live anywhere else?'

Another siren wails, overtakes him. It is a city of banshees. On Pitfield Street he sees a blond curly-haired woman weeping, bulging brown satchel swinging from her shoulder as she heaves tears onto the cracked pavement. Red brake lights throb, reflect in the sweatsheen of his forehead. They say all the trees in this part of the city were planted in memoriam of those lost in the bombings. You can tell which buildings were destroyed by the colour of the brick. The air has cooled in darkness; cycling with one hand he uses the other to pull the zip of his luminous jacket all the way up.

'There's something about it I love, but at the same time it's so… oppressive.'

'Yea! The queues… the civil… obedience. Look at the bar, for example. Where I come from, people don't stand patiently and wait their turn. And bartenders are *agile*. They can multi-task. They know who's next—'

'—The beer here *is* shit.'

'Unless you get into the ales… But bartenders are like *acrobats* where I come from. Here, everyone seems to have been lulled into this kind of bureaucratic, catatonic state. They're half-alive. The city is like a waiting room, you know, with a *really long* wait… I have a theory you know. About that. I used to work for a gardener, and there's this thing call topiary, where you shape bushes.'

'I know it. You see it in period films: big gardens, unicorn bushes and things.'

'Exactly! Well I think this city has that effect on people. Like it shapes them psychologically. It moulds our psychic topiary. All the queues… the systems… traffic lights… loyalty cards… police presence… directions… smartphones… zebra crossings… tenancy agreements and agency fees… supermarket checkouts… a life punctuated by beeps, your oystercard, TfL barriers… It all shapes our pysches, turns us into these obedient beings by applying and setting the boundaries of our daily experience…'

'…'

'…'

'So did you like gardening?'

'What?'

'It must have been hard work?'

'…'

'What's the funniest bush you ever trimmed? Oh! I'm being naughty!'

Outside a pub, the smokers gather in smoking zones. It is still early, and they are unsure of themselves. The red glow of their cigarette-drags leaves a trail on his vision: it seems to him suddenly that the whole city is this star system, this universe of different light sources, elemental, electric, holy, digital. But then other times he has thought of the city as some immense insect, with a trillion tiny light bulb eyes, perched on green land, feeding and shitting where it feeds. Twitching. Vibrating. Grooming itself. And the cyclist himself? Neither living nor dead.

Under a dull moon he finally arrives at the empty office building where JP has been a live-in caretaker for the last few months, swinging the bike into the doorway as people stumble by. The street is awash with betting slips and chicken bones.

'Welcome to the office!' JP beams as he lets the cyclist in with a realistic handshake. Mentally, the cyclist dismounts into the reality of an empty downstairs office, where the carpet has been stripped and the desks and office chairs are piled up on each other and workplace posters still adorn the blue-taced walls. Have you washed your hands?

'I don't use this room,' JP confirms, as the cyclist leans the bike against the bureaucratic paraphernalia: filing cabinets and pedestal lockers piled high with stacks of damp A4 paper, pen-holders, out-trays, staplers, keyboards, old forms…

JP shows him then an industrial kitchen, with buzzing fluorescent light, and toilets marked separately for males and females.

'I like to use the ladies,' JP quips, 'but I know you prefer the gents.'

'They even have hand dryers.'

The building is old, and dampness manifests in corners of the stairwell, rising in clouds up the walls. Upstairs, JP shows him other rooms, packed high with mouldy stock in sagging cardboard boxes. The caretaker's own quarters are at the top of the building and through heavy curtains overlook the typical street: chicken shop, corner off-licence, betting shop, launderette. The room itself is lamplit, warm, with a single made bed, a desk with its own geography of stationary and memento, and the bookshelves he has lugged with him from empty office to empty office over his years in London. It is the cheap rent that lures him, the cheap rent that liberates him.

'Do you fancy a game of chess?' he asks the cyclist after he has shown him out onto the flat roof and they have gazed over the rooftops and chimneys as far as dark St. Paul's. 'I have a few cans of Jamaican Stripe too?'

The cyclist agrees with a shrug and they descend towards the depths of the building again, to play a game in the industrial kitchen.

THE GREATEST SHOW ON EARTH! NOW ON ITS FINAL RUN!

Great mysteries, old stories, bizarre incidents, down there beneath the trembling pavements of the noisy metropolitan zone, beneath how many tons of earth and rubble, in the tiled dimension, where he grows obtuse, grotesque and slanted, in the tunnel corner's convex mirror, as he swivels, bashes elbows with a lesser man coming the opposite way, neither man stopping, never, and the minutes and the seconds not waiting either for these petty collisions to resolve themselves, but all hurtle on, in this tunnel, phone frantically seeking the network, the device desperate, like him, to perform at the highest speed possible, without interruptions or complications, and as he is told by punctuating posters which books to read, which films to watch, a warm wind, a tunnel sirocco, thrusts past him, generating itself from the depths, a child of the darkness of the tunnel, a thousand dark junctions beyond, through twists and turns to countless platforms like specks of deep space dust, and he—the city worker, the passenger—recognises all of this only as the coming of a train, and he breaks into a trot, his briefcase a pendulum axis, propelling him to his platform in double time, his mac tails falling out in his slipstream, lifted by speed of motion and the velocity of the tunnel sirocco, as he takes the final flight of stairs three at a time before glancing left to see his train, and it must be this train—not the train in one minute, or the train in three minutes, or the train in five minutes—and his synapses fire the alarm as he recognises the throngs of people wedged into the carriage but anyway throws himself through the beeping carriage doors, everything beeping, his phone, the doors, the TfL announcements, and he is through all, already calling out to the crowd, 'CAN YOU MOVE DOWN, PLEASE?' as he grasps for a rail to hold onto, because the doors are going to close on him, but he will not be thwarted in his attempt to board this very train, calling louder, 'CAN YOU MOVE DOWN, PLEASE, FOR GOD'S SAKE?' and as he presses against damp, warm bodies, as he leans and pants and huffs and tuts and sighs and earns his space, a voice tells him to stand clear of the closing doors and he is in, he has earned it, and with a jerk that very train pulls away from the fluorescent light of the platform into darkness.

A moment to breathe.

To find some extra space.

To remove his phone from his pocket.

To drop his briefcase between his ankles, the words DRY RISER INLET echoing in his mind's vision.

Lost in the depths of the underground, the dark tunnels beneath clear thought and understanding, the passenger is free to feed on the various entertainments: smartphone, kindle, *METRO* newspaper… Reality is not experienced any longer, it is consumed. And they have not had to wait so long for it, now, have they? It was only a few tunnels. It was only the distance between two points, dots on a map, a sequence of signposts that by now are known by heart. He looks up from his phone's applications to cast bitter, impatient glances at all those who interfere with his personal space, who clog public walkways. Beneath the deafening keen of the train's many carriages, the chain of electric light in the tenebrous black, mice scurry. They have learned to live down here.

Stand back, train approaching. Who among you have not stood back? Stand back! He is the first to emerge as the doors beep beep rapidly and slide open, revealing Him, chest thrust out and already alighting, marching for the stairs. He has reached His destination. The barriers await the loving flick of His Oyster wrist. His name is Bob Moran. He is a Contracts Manager, who lives no more than seventy feet from his tube stop, in Zone Three, over a convenience store, in a one-bed apartment, bills and council tax and water charges included. He will not learn to pronounce his landlord's name. We shelter him from great psychic pain, from the wonder that loss of self brings, from the terror of the Emptiness, of the fragments he has become. He will cry great salt oceans of tears the day we stop distracting him.

REPORT ALL UNATTENDED ITEMS TO A MEMBER OF STAFF

Rachel's thoughts of the future lost to objects, here is a list of things she saw from
the departing train:

bent steel rods poking out of the mud like the
rib cage of some ancient animal skeleton

car parks

scaffolding

empty playgrounds

hundreds of graffiti-ed
codes and secrets

puddled back yards, untidied

rubbish, litter, sinking into the wet bank

waste piping, cable and copper

pipe and vent systems, and clustered satellites on the hidden sides of houses

drab parks with shimmering paths

soggy timber

lonely copses of crooked trees
fences: rusted, aluminium, wooden, chain…

overpasses
underpasses

electricity cables

a low-lying, muddy lake

rotting vegetation

mysterious number-coded signposts

manicured graveyards

yellow flowering gorse

melting snow glistening and trickling from a steep
terrace roof, the water gleaming on the edges of the slate

a motor scrapyard, vehicle roofs green with mould or moss or slime

planks piled neatly against cavity block walls

rusty blue containers in shapeless yards

long-lost traffic cones

gothic windows

high-heeled shoes

warehouses

allotments

a burlesque mannequin with a gas mask over the face

tunnel darkness

her reflection, looking back at her, quite seriously

HAVE YOU TOPPED UP YOUR OYSTER?

Branches thin as fish bones are thrust up towards ashy buds of cloud, as if in offering. Traffic lights, streetlamps, electricity poles, chimneys: all stand erect, stiffened by duty over time, felled only by the most violent abruptions. A stolen car, careering; a mis-manoeuvred shopping delivery… The city tarmac courses through thousands of serpentine pathways, where lorries and buses rumble and luminous cyclists squeeze between on tightropes of space. This is a land of railings mysteriously bent, of warped tile rooftops, of irregular traffic, and the sun rising and falling, trying always to hit every spot in every alleyway, but failing always, with always some chewing-gum pocked dead-end left in cold greyness. Bombs fell once, everywhere. Bombs pounded us.

Smoke drifts from vents and exhausts and chimney shafts. The blue of the sky lemons in the evening. Traffic lights grow and throb. A hula is thrown high in the air one last time before the playground empties. With the light diminished, the thick fat thud of the basketball's bounce can only be heard now, accompanied by the scuffed movements of the evening kids who throw it.

'That is *moist!*'

'Allow it! Allow it!'

The ball's bounce recedes into shadow. The overpass suddenly looms, threatens, the broken glass dimsparkling orange in the streetlit gloom. Countless dark windows. The cycle lane is dangerous now. Hooded men linger.

'Say something constructive!' comes the argument's echo.

Conway. Murphy. We built this city. We love the gentle hush of the M25 as the traffic collects itself and begins to breathe gently, sleepily, calmly surging into the pink dawn.

NOTES ON CONTRIBUTORS

Gary Allen has published thirteen collections, most recently, *Mexico* (Agenda Editions, 2013). A new collection, *Jackson's Corner*, is due this year from Greenwich Exchange. His poems have been published widely, in journals including *Alaskan Quarterly Review, Australian Book Review, Ambit, Fiddlehead, London Magazine, Malahat Review, The Poetry Review, Prairie Schooner, Stand, The Threepenny Review*.

Sarah Barnsley was shortlisted for an Eric Gregory Award (2004), the Bridport Prize (2010), and was joint runner-up in the Poetry School/Pighog Pamphlet Competition (2014). She has published in a range of magazines; her pamphlet, *The Fire Station*, is forthcoming from Telltale Press. Sarah teaches at Goldsmiths, University of London.

Kevin Barry is the author of the International IMPAC Dublin Literary Award winning novel, *City of Bohane*, and two short-story collections, *There Are Little Kingdoms*— published by The Stinging Fly Press—and *Dark Lies The Island*. His new novel, *Beatlebone*, will be published by Canongate in November 2015. 'monologue for cabman' was written as part of a collaboration with London-based Irish artist Kathy Prendergast.

Claire-Louise Bennett's short fiction and essays have been published in various magazines. In 2013 she won the inaugural White Review Short Story Prize. She has been awarded bursaries by Galway City Council and The Arts Council. The Stinging Fly Press published her first collection of stories, *Pond*, in April this year. It will be published in the UK by Fitzcarraldo in the autumn.

Daniel Bennett was born in Shropshire, and lives in London. He is the author of the novel *All The Dogs*. Find him on Twitter: @AbsenceClub.

Harry Clifton was Ireland Professor of Poetry from 2010 to 2013. The poem in this issue is included in *The Holding Centre: Selected Poems 1974-2004*, published last year by Bloodaxe Books and Wake Forest. *Ireland and its Elsewheres*, his professorship lectures, will be published later this year by University College Dublin Press.

Evelyn Conlon has published three short story collections and four novels, most recently *Not The Same Sky*. She lives in Dublin, where she is a member of Aosdána.

Gavin Corbett's second novel, *This Is the Way*, is published by Fourth Estate. It was named 2013 Kerry Group Irish Novel of the Year and shortlisted for the Encore Award. His latest novel, *Green Glowing Skull*, was published in May 2015.

Danny Denton is from Cork, but currently lives in London. Employments include: labourer, barman, data entry clerk, journalist, writer of contracts and teacher. Work has appeared in various journals, anthologies and newspapers; at the moment he is resolving a novel set in an Ireland where it always rains.

Rob Doyle's novel, *Here Are the Young Men*, was chosen as a book of the year for 2014 in *The Irish Times*, *Sunday Times*, *Sunday Business Post*, and *The Independent* (UK). His second book, *This Is the Ritual*, will be published in January 2016 (Bloomsbury / Lilliput).

Martina Evans is the author of ten books of prose and poetry. Her latest collection *Burnfort Las Vegas* was shortlisted for the Irish Times Poetry Now Award 2015 and *Mountainy Men*, a work-in-progress, won a Grants for the Arts Award in April 2015. She is an associate lecturer in Creative Writing at Birkbeck, University of London, and lector for the Royal Literary Fund Reading Round 2014-2016.

Catherine Higgins-Moore holds a Masters in Creative Writing from the University of Oxford and an undergraduate degree from Trinity College Dublin. She has been shortlisted for the Asham Award, Cambridge University's Jane Martin Poetry Prize and the HG Wells Grand Prize. She is editor of *The Irish Literary Review*.

Maurice Leitch was born in County Antrim and is the author of novels, short stories, radio and television plays and documentaries. *Poor Lazarus* won the Guardian Fiction Prize in 1969, and *Silver's City* the Whitbread in 1981. He was awarded an MBE in 1999 for services to Literature. His latest novel, *Seeking Mr Hare*, was published in 2013.

Patrick McCabe was born in Clones, County Monaghan, where he still lives, in 1955. He has worked a lot in fiction and drama and published a lot over the years. At the moment he is working with Corcadorca, Cork, on a new play, and on a number of stories. He likes music but not football.

Danielle McLaughlin's short stories have appeared in newspapers and magazines such as *The Stinging Fly*, *The Irish Times*, *The South Circular*, *Southword*, *The Penny Dreadful*, *Long Story, Short* and *The New Yorker*. Her debut collection, *Dinosaurs on Other Planets*, will be published in October 2015 by The Stinging Fly Press.

Niamh Mulvey is from Kilkenny. She studied at NUI Galway and worked in a variety of jobs before moving to London to work in publishing. She is now Acting Editorial Director at Quercus Children's Books. She lives in south-east London.

Tony Murray is Director of the Irish Studies Centre at London Metropolitan University. He is curator of the Archive of the Irish in Britain and runs the annual Irish Writers in London Summer School. He researches literary and cultural representations of the Irish diaspora, and his book *London Irish Fictions: Narrative, Diaspora and Identity* was published in paperback by Liverpool University Press last year.

David Nash was born in County Cork, and currently lives in London. He has had poems published in several magazines and anthologies, and is working on his first collection.

Mary Noonan lives in Cork. Her poems have appeared in numerous magazines. Her first collection, *The Fado House* (Dedalus Press, Dublin, 2012), was shortlisted for the Seamus Heaney Centre Prize and the Strong/Shine Award.

Edna O'Brien has written over twenty works of fiction along with plays, memoirs and biographies. Awards received include the Irish Pen Lifetime Achievement Award, the American National Arts Gold Medal, The Frank O'Connor Short Story Award and the Ulysses Medal. Her most recent book is *The Love Object: Selected Stories*.

Sean O'Reilly is the author of *Curfew and Other Stories, Love and Sleep, The Swing of Things* and *Watermark*. He teaches regularly in the Irish Writers Centre and leads the Stinging Fly fiction workshops.

Michael Ray is a visual artist, who grew up in Sussex, and now lives in West Cork. He has an emotional attachment to London as it was the location of a significant relationship. He has been published in a number of journals including *The Shop, The Moth, Cyphers, One, Magma* and *Ambit*.

Pádraigín Riggs lectured in the Department of Modern Irish, UCC, before her retirement. Her publications include a study of the short story writer, Donncha Ó Ceileachair and a literary biography of Pádraic Ó Conaire as well as numerous articles on modern literature in Irish and on the cultural and intellectual history of the London Irish.

Declan Ryan was born in County Mayo. He teaches at King's College London and is poetry editor at *Ambit*. His debut pamphlet appeared in the Faber New Poets series in 2014.

Cathy Sweeney has published short stories in *The Stinging Fly* and *The Dublin Review*. A story of hers is included in the anthology *Young Irelanders* (New Island, 2015), edited by Dave Lordan.

Matthew Sweeney's most recent collection, *Horse Music* (Bloodaxe Books, 2013), won the inaugural Piggott Poetry Prize in 2014. A new collection, *Inquisition Lane*, is forthcoming from Bloodaxe Books in September 2015.

Joanna Walsh's stories are published by Granta, Dalkey, Salt, and others. Her books include *Fractals* (2013), *Hotel* (2015) and *Vertigo* (2015). She writes for *The Guardian, The New Statesman* and *The National*, edits at *3:AM Magazine*, and runs @ read_women.

Clair Wills is Chair of Irish Letters at the University of Princeton. She is currently writing a history of Britain in the 1950s and 60s, told from the perspective of migrants from Europe, the Caribbean and South Asia.